THE GLENCOE LITERATURE LIBRARY

...And the Earth Did Not Devour Him

and Related Readings

Glencoe McGraw-Hill

New York, New York   Columbus, Ohio   Woodland Hills, California   Peoria, Illinois

Acknowledgments

Grateful acknowledgment is given authors, publishers, photographers, museums, and agents for permission to reprint the following copyrighted material. Every effort has been made to determine copyright owners. In case of any omissions, the Publisher will be pleased to make suitable acknowledgments in future editions.

. . . Y NO LO TRAGO LA TIERRA/. . . AND THE EARTH DID NOT DEVOUR HIM by Tomás Rivera is reprinted with permission from the publisher (Houston: Arte Publico Press— University of Houston, 1987)

"Working in *La Fresa*," José Luis Ríos; "My *Familia*," Victor Machuca, "*Fitting In*," Andrea Martínez. Interviews from VOICES FROM THE FIELDS by S. Beth Atkin. Copyright © 1993 by S. Beth Atkin. By permission of Little, Brown and Company.

"Christmas" from NOT WITHOUT LAUGHTER by Langston Hughes. Copyright © 1930 by Alfred A. Knopf, Inc. Reprinted by permission of the publisher.

"Children for Hire" by Verena Dobnik and Ted Anthony. Copyright © 1997 Associated Press, reprinted by permission.

"First Confession" from COLLECTED STORIES by Frank O'Connor. Copyright © 1951 by Frank O'Connor. Reprinted by permission of Alfred A. Knopf, Inc., and by arrangement with Harriet O'Donovan Sheehy, c/o Joan Daves Agency as agent for the proprietor.

"Aria: A Memoir of a Bilingual Childhood" from HUNGER OF MEMORY by Richard Rodriguez (Boston: David R. Godine, Publisher, 1981). Copyright © 1981 by Richard Rodriguez. Reprinted by permission of George Borchardt, Inc. for the author.

Cover Art: Private Collection/Christie's Images/Bridgeman Art Library

Glencoe/McGraw-Hill

A Division of The **McGraw·Hill** *Companies*

Send all inquiries to:
Glencoe/McGraw-Hill
8787 Orion Place
Columbus, OH 43240

ISBN 0-02-817978-1
Printed in the United States of America
2 3 4 5 6 7 8 9 026 04 03 02 01 00

Contents

Contents Continued

Related Readings   65

...And the Earth Did Not Devour Him

Tomás Rivera

Translation by
Evangelina Vigil-Piñón

The Lost Year

THAT YEAR WAS LOST TO HIM. At times he tried to remember and, just about when he thought everything was clearing up some, he would be at a loss for words. It almost always began with a dream in which he would suddenly awaken and then realize that he was really asleep. Then he wouldn't know whether what he was thinking had happened or not.

It always began when he would hear someone calling him by his name but when he turned his head to see who was calling, he would make a complete turn and there he would end up—in the same place. This was why he never could discover who was calling him nor why. And then he even forgot the name he had been called.

One time he stopped at mid-turn and fear suddenly set in. He realized that he had called himself. And thus the lost year began.

He tried to figure out when that time he had come to call "year" had started. He became aware that he was always thinking and thinking and from this there was no way out. Then he started thinking about how he never thought and this was when his mind would go blank and he would fall asleep. But before falling asleep he saw and heard many things . . .

WHAT HIS MOTHER NEVER KNEW was that every night he would drink the glass of water that she left under the bed for spirits. She always believed that they drank the water and so she continued doing her duty. Once he was going to tell her but then he thought that he'd wait and tell her when he was grown up.

The Children
Couldn't Wait

The heat had set in with severity. This was unusual because it was only the beginning of April and this kind of heat was not expected until the end of the month. It was so hot that the bucket of water the boss brought them was not enough. He would come only two times for the midday and sometimes they couldn't hold out. That was why they took to drinking water from a tank at the edge of the furrow. The boss had it there for the cattle and when he caught them drinking water there he got angry. He didn't much like the idea of their losing time going to drink water because they weren't on contract, but by the hour. He told them that if he caught them there again he was going to fire them and not pay them. The children were the ones who couldn't wait.

"I'm very thirsty, Dad. Is the boss gonna be here soon?"

"I think so. You can't wait any longer?"

"Well, I don't know. My throat already feels real dry. Do you think he's almost gonna be here? Should I go to the tank?"

"No, wait just a little longer. You already heard what he said."

"I know, that he'll fire us if he catches us there, but I can't wait."

"Come on now, come on, work. He'll be here real soon."

"Well . . . I'll try to wait. Why doesn't this one let us bring water? Up north . . . "

"Because he's no good, that's why."

"But we could hide it under the seat, couldn't we? It was always better up north . . . And what if I make like I'm gonna go relieve myself by the tank?"

And this was what they started doing that afternoon. They pretended they were going to relieve themselves and they would go on to the edge of the tank. The boss became aware of this almost right away. But he didn't let on. He wanted to catch a bunch of them and that way he could pay fewer of them and only after they had done more work. He noticed that one of the children kept going to drink water every little while and he became more and more furious. He thought then of giving him a scare and he crawled on the ground to get his rifle.

What he set out to do and what he did were two different things. He shot at him once to scare him but when he pulled the trigger he saw the boy with a hole in his head. And the child didn't even jump like a deer does. He just stayed in the water like a dirty rag and the water began to turn bloody . . .

"They say that the old man almost went crazy."

"You think so?"

"Yes, he's already lost the ranch. He hit the bottle pretty hard. And then after they tried him and he got off free, they say he jumped off a tree 'cause he wanted to kill himself."

"But he didn't kill himself, did he?"

"Well, no."

"Well, there you have it."

"Well, I'll tell you, compadre, I think he did go crazy. You've seen the likes of him nowadays. He looks like a beggar."

"Sure, but that's 'cause he doesn't have any more money."

"Well . . . that's true."

SHE HAD FALLEN ASLEEP right away and everyone, very mindful of not crossing their arms nor their legs nor their hands, watched her intensely. The spirit was already present in her body.

"Let's see, how may I help you this evening, brothers and sisters?"

"Well, you see, I haven't heard from my boy in two months. Yesterday a letter from the government arrived telling me that he's lost in action. I'd like to know whether or not he's alive. I feel like I'm losing my mind just thinking and thinking about it."

"Have no fear, sister. Julianito is fine. He's just fine. Don't worry about him anymore. Very soon he'll be in your arms. He'll be returning already next month."

"Thank you, thank you."

A Prayer

DEAR GOD, JESUS CHRIST, keeper of my soul. This is the third Sunday that I come to implore you, beg you, to give me word of my son. I have not heard from him. Protect him, my God, that no bullet may pierce his heart like it happened to Doña Virginia's son, may he rest in God's peace. Take care of him for me, Dear Jesus, save him from the gunfire, have pity on him who is so good. Since he was a baby, when I would nurse him to sleep, he was so gentle, very grateful, never biting me. He's very innocent, protect him, he does not wish to harm anyone, he is very noble, he is very kind, may no bullet pierce his heart.

Please, Virgin Mary, you, too, shelter him. Shield his body, cover his head, cover the eyes of the Communists and the Koreans and the Chinese so that they cannot see him, so they won't kill him. I still keep his toys from when he was a child, his little cars, little trucks, even a kite that I found the other day in the closet. Also his cards and the funnies that he has learned to read. I have put everything away until his return.

Protect him, Jesus, that they may not kill him. I have made a promise to the Virgen de San Juan to pay her homage at her shrine and to the Virgen de Guadalupe, too. He also wears a little medallion of the Virgen de San Juan del Valle and he, too, has made a promise to her; he wants to live. Take care of him, cover his heart with your hand, that no bullet may enter it. He's very noble. He was very afraid to go, he told me so. The day they took him, when he said his farewell he embraced me and he cried for a while. I could feel his heart beating and I remembered when he was little and I would nurse him and the happiness that I felt and he felt.

Take care of him for me, please, I beseech you. I promise you my life for his. Bring him back from Korea safe and sound. Cover his heart with your hands. Jesus Christ, Holy God, Virgen de Guadalupe, bring him back alive, bring me back his heart. Why have they taken him? He has done no harm. He knows nothing. He is very humble. He doesn't want to take away anybody's life. Bring him back alive, I don't want him to die.

Here is my heart for his. Here is my heart. Here in my chest, palpitating. Tear it out if blood is what you want, but tear it out of me. I sacrifice my heart for his. Here it is. Here is my heart! Through it runs his very own blood . . .

Bring him back alive and I will give you my very own heart.

COMADRE, DO YOU ALL PLAN TO GO TO UTAH?"

"No, compadre. I'll tell you, we don't trust the man that's contracting people to go work in—how do you say it?"

"Utah. Why, comadre?"

"Because we don't think there's such a state. You tell me, when've you ever heard of that place?"

"Well, there's so many states. And this is the first time that they've contracted for work in those parts."

"Yeah, but tell me, where is it?"

"Well, we've never been there but I hear it's somewhere close to Japan."

It's That
It Hurts

IT HURTS A LOT. That's why I hit him. And now what do I do? Maybe they didn't expel me from school. Maybe it ain't so, after all. Maybe it's not. *Sure it is!* It is so, they did expel me. And now what do I do?

I think it all started when I got so embarrassed and angry at the same time. I dread getting home. What am I going to tell Mother? And then when Dad gets home from the fields? They'll whip me for sure. But it's embarrassing and angering. It's always the same in these schools in the north. Everybody just stares at you up and down. And then they make fun of you and the teacher with her popsicle stick, poking your head for lice. It's embarrassing. And then when they turn up their noses. It makes you angry. I think it's better staying out here on the ranch, here in the quiet of this knoll, with its chicken coops, or out in the fields where you at least feel more free, more at ease.

> "Come on, son, we're almost there."
> "You gonna take me to the principal?"
> "Of course not. Don't tell me you don't know how to speak English yet. Look, that's the entrance over there. Just ask if you don't know where to go. Don't be shy, ask someone. Don't be afraid."
> "Why can't you go in with me?"
> "Don't tell me you're scared. Look, that's probably the entrance there. Here comes someone. Now, you behave, you hear me?"
> "But why don't you help me?"
> "No. You'll do just fine, don't be afraid."

It's always the same. They take you to the nurse and the first thing she does is check you for lice. And, too, those ladies are to blame. On Sundays they sit out in front of the chicken coops picking lice from each other's heads. And the gringos, passing by in their cars, looking and pointing at them. Dad is right when he says that they look like monkeys in the zoo. But it's not all that bad.

"Mother, you won't believe it. They took me out of the room. I had just walked in, and they put me in with a nurse all dressed in white. And they made me take off my clothes and they even examined my behind. But where they took the longest was on my head. I had washed it, right? Well, the nurse brought out a jar of, like vaseline, it smelled like worm-killer, do I still smell? And she smeared it all over my head. It itched. And then she started parting my hair with a pencil. After a while they let me go but I was so ashamed because I had to take off my pants, even my underwear, in front of the nurse."

But now what do I tell them? That they threw me out of school? But it wasn't all my fault. I didn't like that gringo, right off. This one didn't laugh at me. He'd just stare and when they put me in the corner apart from everyone he kept turning to look at me, and then he'd make a gesture with his finger. I was mad but mostly I felt embarrassed because I was sitting away from everyone where they could see me better. Then when it was my turn to read, I couldn't. I could hear myself. And I could hear that no words were coming out . . . This cemetery isn't scarey at all. That's what I like best about the walk to school and back. The greenness! And everything so even. The roads all paved. It even looks like where they play golf. Today I won't have time to run up the hills and slide down tumbling. Nor to lie down on the grass and try to hear all the sounds. Last time I counted to 26 . . . If I hurry maybe I can go to the dump with Doña Cuquita. She heads out about this time when the sun's not so hot.

"Careful, children. Just be careful and don't step where there's fire burning underneath. Wherever you see smoke coming out, there's coals underneath. I know what I'm telling you, I once got a bad burn and I still have the scar . . . Look, each of you get a long stick and just turn the trash over briskly. If the dump man comes to see what we're doing, tell him we came to throw away some stuff. He's a kind man, but he likes to keep those little books with nasty pictures that people sometimes throw away . . . watch out for the train as you cross that bridge. It ran over a man last year . . . caught him right in middle of the bridge and he wasn't able to make it to the other side . . . Did they give you permission to come with me? . . . Don't eat anything until after you've washed it."

But if I go with her without permission they'll whip me even more. What am I going to tell them? Maybe they didn't expel me. *Sure, they did!* Maybe not. *Yeah, they did!* What am I going to tell them? But it wasn't all my fault. I couldn't wait anymore. While I was standing there in the restroom he's the one that started picking on me.

> "Hey, Mex . . . I don't like Mexicans because they steal. You hear me?"
> "Yes."
> "I don't like Mexicans. You hear, Mex?"
> "Yes."
> "I don't like Mexicans because they steal. You hear me?"
> "Yes."

I remember the first fight I had at school, I got real scared because everything happened so slow. There wasn't any reason, it's just that some of the older boys who already had mustaches and who were still in the second grade started pushing us against each other. And they kept it up until we started fighting, I think, 'cause we were plain scared. It was about a block from school, I remember, when they started pushing me towards Ramiro. Then we began to scuffle and hit at each other. Some ladies came out and broke us up. Since then I got to feeling bigger. But all it was, up until I fought, was plain fear.

This time it was different. He didn't warn me. I just felt a real hard blow on my ear and I heard something like when you put a conch to your ear at the beach. I don't remember anymore how or when I hit him but I know I did because someone told the principal that we were fighting in the restroom. Maybe they didn't throw me out? *Sure they did!* And then, I wonder who called the principal? And the janitor all scared and with his broom up in the air, ready to swat me if I tried to leave.

> "The Mexican kid got into a fight and beat up a couple of our boys . . . No, not bad . . . but what do I do?"
> " . . . "
> "No, I guess not, they could care less if I expel him . . . They need him in the fields."
> " . . . "
> "Well, I just hope our boys don't make too much out about it to their parents. I guess I'll just throw him out."
> " . . . "
> "Yeah, I guess you're right."
> " . . . "
> "I know you warned me, I know, I know . . . but . . . yeah, ok."

But how could I even think of leaving knowing that everyone at home wanted me to go to school. Anyways, the janitor stood with his broom up in the air, ready for anything . . . And then they just told me to leave.

I'm halfway home. This cemetery is real pretty. It doesn't look anything like the one in Texas. That one *is* scarey, I don't like it at all. What scares me the most is when we're leaving after a burial and I look up and I read the letters on the arch over the gate that say, *Don't forget me.* It's like I can hear all the dead people buried there saying these words and then the sound of these words stays in my mind and sometimes even if I don't look up when I pass through the gate, I still see them. But not this one, this one is real pretty. Just lots of soft grass and trees, I guess that's why here when people bury somebody they don't even cry. I like playing here. If only they would let us fish in the little creek that runs through here, there's lots of fish. But no, you even need a license to fish and then they don't even sell us one 'cause we're from out of state.

I won't be able to go to school anymore. What am I going to tell them? They've told me over and over that our teachers are like our second parents . . . and now? And when we get back to Texas everyone will find out too. Mother and Dad will be angry; I might get more than just a whipping. And then my Uncle will find out and Grandpa. Maybe they might even send me to a reform school like the ones I've heard them talk about. There they turn you into a good person if you're bad. They're real hard on you. They leave you soft as a glove. But maybe they didn't expel me, *sure they did,* maybe not, *sure they did.* I could make like I'm going to school and stay here in the cemetery. That would be better. But then what? I could tell them that I lost my report card. And then what if I stay in the same grade? What hurt me the most is that now I won't be able to be a telephone operator like Dad wants me to. You need to finish school for that.

> "Vieja, call m'ijo out here . . . look, compadre, ask your godson what he wants to be when he grows up and finishes school."
>
> "What will you be, godson?"
>
> "I don't know."
>
> "Tell him! Don't be embarrassed. He's your godfather."
>
> "What will you be, son ?"
>
> "A telephone operator."
>
> "Is that so?"
>
> "Yes, compadre, he's very determined, you know that? Every time we ask him he says he wants to be an operator. I think they pay well. I told the boss the other day and he laughed. I don't think he believes that my son can do it, but that's 'cause he doesn't know him. He's smarter than anything. I just pray God helps him finish school so he can become an operator."

That movie was good. The operator was the most important one. Ever since then I suppose that's why Dad has wanted me to study for that after I finish school. But . . . maybe they didn't throw me out. What if it's not true? Maybe not. *Sure, it is.* What do I tell them? What do I do? Now they won't be able to ask me what I'm going to be when I grow up. Maybe not. *No, yeah.* What do I do? It's that it hurts and it's embarrassing at the same time. I better just stay here. No, but then Mother will get scared like she does when there's lightning and thunder. I've gotta tell them. And when my padrino comes to visit us I'll just hide. No need for him to find out. Nor for me to read to him like Dad has me do every time he comes to visit us. What I'll do when he comes is hide behind the chest or under the bed. That way Dad and Mother won't feel embarrassed. And what if I really wasn't expelled? Maybe I wasn't? *No, yeah.*

WHY DO Y'ALL GO TO SCHOOL SO MUCH?"

"My Dad says it's to prepare us. He says that if someday there's an opportunity, maybe they'll give it to us."

"Sure! If I were you I wouldn't worry about that. The poor can't get poorer. We can't get worst off than we already are. That's why I don't worry. The ones who have to be on their toes are the ones who are higher up. They've got something to lose. They can end up where we're at. But for us what does it matter?"

Hand in
His Pocket

REMEMBER DON LAÍTO and Doña Bone? That's what everyone called them but their names were Don Hilario and Doña Bonifacia. Don't you remember? Well, I had to live with them for three weeks until school ended. At first I liked it but then later on I didn't.

Everything that people used to say about them behind their backs was true. About how they baked the bread, the pastries, how they would sometimes steal and that they were bootleggers. I saw it all. Anyways, they were good people but by the time school was about to end I was afraid of being with them in that Model-T that they had and even of sleeping in their house. And towards the end I didn't even feel like eating. That's why I'd go to the little neighborhood store to buy me some candy. And that's how I got along until my Dad, my Mother and my brothers and sisters came to get me.

I remember they were very nice to me on the first day. Don Laíto laughed a lot and you could see his gold teeth and the rotten ones, too. And every little while Doña Bone, fat as could be, would grab me and squeeze me against her and I could feel her, real fat. They fed me dinner—I say *fed* me because *they* didn't eat. Now that I'm remembering, you know, I never saw them eat. The meat that she fried for me was green and it smelled really bad when she was cooking it. But after a while it didn't smell as much. But I don't know whether this was because I got used to the smell or because Don Laíto opened the window. Just parts of it tasted bad. I ate it all because I didn't want to hurt their feelings. Everybody liked Don Laíto and Doña Bone. Even the Anglos were fond of them. They gave them canned foods, clothes, toys. And when Don Laíto and Doña Bone weren't able to sell these to us, they'd give them to us. They would also pay us visits out in the fields to sell us Mexican sweetbread, thread and needles, canned food and nopalitos, and also shoes, coats and other things that sometimes were good, sometimes pretty bad.

"Won't you buy these shoes . . . oh, come on . . . I know they're used, but they're the expensive kind . . . look how they're not worn out yet . . . these . . . I guarantee you, they last until they wear out . . . "

I didn't want to seem ungrateful, so I ate it all. It made me sick. I had to spend a long time in the restroom. The worst of it was when I went to bed. They put me in a room with no light and that smelled musty and was crowded with things: boxes, bottles, almanacs, bundles of clothing. There was only one entrance. You couldn't even see the windows with so many things all piled up. The first night I hardly slept because I was sure that spiders would be crawling down from the hole in the ceiling. Everything smelled so awful. By the time it grew dark I couldn't see anything, but it must have been around midnight when I woke up. I think I had fallen asleep, but I'm not too sure. The only thing I could see was that real dark hole in the ceiling. It seemed I could see faces but it was just my imagination. In any case, fear got the best of me. And I wasn't able to sleep anymore. Only at dawn when I could see the rest of the things in the room. Sometimes I would imagine Don Laíto and Doña Bone seated around me and there were times when I would even reach my hand out to touch them, but there was nothing. I think that from that very first day I wanted them to come get me. Something in my heart told me that something would happen. It's not that they weren't good people, they were, but like they say, they had their bad side.

At school, classes were going well. Sometimes when I came back from school in the afternoon not a sound could be heard in the small house and it seemed like no one was around. But always, when I was feeling most at peace, Doña Bone would scare me. She'd grab me from behind and laugh, and me, I'd jump, I was so scared. And she would just laugh and laugh. The first few times I'd end up laughing too, but later I got tired of it. Then later on they told me bit by bit what they would do when they went downtown. They stole lots of things: food, liquor, clothes, cigarettes, even meat. When they weren't able to sell it to the neighbors, they gave it away. They would get rid of almost everything. Another thing, after a few days they invited me to see how they made sweet bread. Don Laíto would take off his shirt. He looked very hairy. He would start sweating as he kneaded the dough. But it was when he would stick his hands under his arms and then keep on kneading the dough that made me the sickest. It was true what people said. He would look at me to see if I was getting nauseous and he would tell me that this was what all the bakers did. One thing for sure, I never again ate any of the sweet bread that he baked, even though they sometimes had a bunch of it on the table.

I remember one day after school they put me to work in the yard. Not that it was so hard, but since that moment they had me working all the time. They wanted me to work at all hours. It's that my Dad had paid them for my board! One time they even wanted me to try to steal a five-pound sack of flour. Can you imagine? I was scared, and besides, it wasn't right.

Don Laíto would just laugh . . . Anyway, the days went on this way until, sometimes, I even felt like leaving, but how could I? My Dad had left me there and he had spent his money. The food got worse, and it got to be all work all the time.

And then . . . I'll tell you something . . . but please don't tell anyone. I noticed that this wetback started coming to the house while Don Laíto was away. I don't know how he knew when he wasn't there. Anyway, if I happened to be inside the house, Doña Bone would throw me out, and if I wasn't inside she would latch the doors and I knew I wasn't supposed to enter. One time Doña Bone tried to explain the whole thing to me but, to be very honest, I felt embarrassed and I hardly heard anything she told me. I did know that he left her money. Whoever he was, he was old and every time he came he smelled of shaving lotion and the smell would linger for a good while after he left. One night I overheard a conversation between the old couple.

> "This guy has money and, besides that, he doesn't have any relatives. Look, viejo, it would be so easy. Not even anyone to worry about him . . . I don't think so, do you? . . . That boss could care less, he darn sure knows that he's a wetback and if something happens to him, you think he'll be concerned about him? Nobody knows that he comes here . . . you just leave it up to me . . . Oh, that'll be so easy . . . "

The next day, after school, they marked a square on the ground in the yard under some trees, and they told me that they wanted to build a cellar and that they wanted me to start digging there, little by little. They were going to use it to store the jars of preserves that Doña Bone made. It took me three days to dig somewhat deep and then they told me to stop digging, that they weren't going to build it after all. And then came the good part.

I remember well that the wetback arrived, his hair combed real good and fragrant, like always. At dusk Doña Bone called me to come eat. There was Don Laíto, already, but I didn't know how he had entered. After dinner they told me to go to bed right away.

I got the scare of my life when I stretched out on the bed and I touched what felt like a snake but what was in reality the wetback's arm. I thought he must be drunk because he didn't wake up. I jumped back and got out of the room. The old couple burst into laughter. Then I noticed that part of my shirt was full of blood. I didn't know what to think. I just remember Don Laíto's gold teeth and his rotten ones.

When it got real dark they made me help them drag him out and throw him into the hole that I myself had dug. As for me, I didn't really want to but then they told me that they would tell the police that I had killed him.

I thought of how my Dad had paid them for my room and board and how even the Anglos liked them so much. All that my parents wanted was for me to finish school so I could find me some job that wasn't so hard. I was real scared but I went ahead and threw him in the hole. Then the three of us threw dirt over him. I never saw his face. All I wanted was for school to end so they would come for me. The two weeks left went by very slowly. I thought that I'd get over my fright or that I'd be able to forget about it, but no. Don Laíto was even wearing the wetback's wrist watch. In the yard you could see the mound of dirt.

When my Dad and my Mother finally came for me they told me that I was very thin and that I looked like I was sick from fright. I told them no, that it was because I played so much at school and after school. Before we left, Don Laíto and Doña Bone squeezed me and told me in loud voices, so that Dad could hear, not to say anything or they would tell the police. Then they started laughing and I noticed that Dad had taken it as a joke. On the way to the farm they talked about how kind Don Laíto and Doña Bone were and how everyone liked them so much. I just kept looking out the car window and telling them yes. After about two months or so, just about when it seemed that I was forgetting all about it, they came to visit us at the farm. They had a present for me. A ring. They made me put it on and I remembered that it was the one the wetback had on that day. As soon as they left I tried to throw it away but I don't know why I couldn't. I thought that someone might find it. And the worst was that for a long time, as soon as I would see a stranger, I'd slip my hand into my pocket. That habit stayed with me for a long time.

It WAS AN HOUR BEFORE the afternoon movie started. He needed a haircut, so he went into the barber shop across the street from the theater. At first he didn't quite understand, so he sat down and waited. But then the barber told him again that he couldn't cut his hair. He thought the barber didn't have time, so he remained seated waiting for the other barber. When he was finished with the client, he got up and walked to the barber's chair. But this barber told him the same thing. That he couldn't cut his hair. Furthermore, he told him that it would be better if he left. He crossed the street and stood there waiting for the theater to open, but then the barber came out and told him to leave. Then it all became clear to him and he went home to get his father.

A Silvery Night

IT WAS A SILVERY NIGHT when he called the devil. Everything was almost clear and it even smelled like day. The whole day he thought about what could happen to him, but the more he thought about it the more curious he became and the less fearful. So that by the time everybody went to bed and turned off the lights, he had already decided to go out right at midnight. He would have to slide across the floor to the door without anyone hearing or seeing him.

"Dad. Why don't you leave the door open. There aren't any mosquitos, anyway."

"Yes, but what if some animal gets in. You remember that badger that got into the Flores' home."

"But that was two years ago. Come on, leave it open. It's real hot. Nothing's gonna get in. All that's left around here are crows, and those don't get into people's houses. Come on. See how all the other people leave their doors open."

"Yes, but at least they've got screens."

"Not all of them. Please. See how pretty the moon looks. Everything is so peaceful."

"All right . . . No, Vieja, no animal is going to crawl in. You and your fears."

The devil had fascinated him as far back as he could remember. Even when they had taken him to the shepherds plays at his Aunt Pana's, he was already curious about how it might look. He thought about Don Rayos, with his black metal mask, with his red horns and black cape. Then he remembered how he found the costume and the mask under Don Rayos' house. One of his marbles had rolled under the house and when he reached for it he found everything all full of dust. He pulled everything out, dusted it off and then he put on the mask.

"I tell you, compadre, you don't fool around with the devil. There are many who have summoned him and have regretted it afterwards. Most of them go insane. Sometimes they get together in groups to summon him, so they won't be afraid. But he doesn't appear before them until later, when each of them is alone, and he appears in different shapes. No, nobody should fool with the devil. If you do, as they say, you give up your soul. Some die of fright, others don't. They just start looking real somber and then they don't even talk anymore. It's like their spirits have left their bodies."

From where he was lying on the floor he could see the clock on the table. He sensed each of his brothers and sisters falling asleep, one by one, and then his parents. He thought he could even make out the sound of snores coming from the other chicken shacks. Eleven to eleven-fifty went by the slowest. Occasionally, he felt somewhat fearful, but then he would look outside where everything was so still and serene under the silvery light of the moon and his fears quickly passed.

"If I leave here at eleven-fifty I'll have enough time to get to the center of the knoll. Good thing there's no snakes here, otherwise it'd be dangerous walking through the weeds that grow so tall at the center of the knoll. I'll call him right at twelve. I better take the clock so I'll know when it's exactly twelve. Otherwise, he might not come. It has to be right at midnight, exactly midnight."

Very slowly, without making a sound, he left, picking up the clock from the table. He put it in his pants' pocket and he noticed that it ticked louder inside the pocket than outside. Even once he was past the chicken coops he walked very slowly, stepping carefully and stopping every now and then. He felt someone was watching him. He proceeded cautiously until he had passed the outhouse. From there the chicken coops were barely visible and he began talking to himself but very softly.

"And how do I call him? Maybe he'll appear. No, I don't think so. In any case, if he does appear he can't do anything to me. I haven't died yet. So he can't do anything to me. I'd just like to know whether there is or isn't . . . If there isn't a devil, maybe there also isn't . . . No, I better not say it. I might get punished. But if there's no devil maybe there's no punishment. No, there has to be punishment. Well, how do I call him? Just, devil? Or, imp? Or, demon? Lucifer? Satan? . . . Whatever comes first."

He got to the center of the knoll and summoned him. At first no words came out, from pure fright, but then his name slipped out in a loud voice and nothing happened. He kept calling him by different names. And nothing. No one came out. Everything looked the same. Everything was the same. All peaceful. Then he thought it would be better to curse the devil instead. So he did. He swore at him using all the cuss words that he knew and in different tones of voice. He even cursed the devil's mother. But nothing. Nothing nor no one appeared, nor did anything change. Disillusioned and feeling at moments a little brave, he headed back for the house. The sound of the wind rustling the leaves of the trees seemed to accompany his every step. There was no devil.

> "But if there's no devil neither is there . . . No, I better not say it. I might get punished. But there's no devil. Maybe he'll appear before me later. No, he would've appeared already. What better time than at night and me, alone? No, there's no devil. There isn't."

Two or three different times he sensed someone calling him but he didn't want to turn around. He didn't get scared because he felt sure that it wasn't anyone nor anything. After he laid down, very careful not to make a sound, certain that there was no devil, he began to feel chills and his stomach became upset. Before falling asleep he thought for a good while. *There is no devil, there is nothing.* The only thing that had been present in the woods was his own voice. No wonder, he thought, people said you shouldn't fool around with the devil. Now he understood everything. Those who summoned the devil went crazy, not because the devil appeared, but just the opposite, because he didn't appear. He fell asleep gazing at the moon as it jumped through the clouds and the trees, as if it were extremely content about something.

ONE AFTERNOON A MINISTER from one of the protestant churches in the town came to the farm and informed them that some man would be coming to teach them manual skills so that they would no longer have to work just in the fields. Practically all of the men got excited. He was going to teach them carpentry. A man came about two weeks later in a station wagon hauling a trailer. He brought with him the minister's wife to assist him as interpreter. But they never taught them anything. They would spend the entire day inside the trailer. A week later they left without a word. They later learned that the man had run off with the minister's wife.

And the Earth Did Not Devour Him

THE FIRST TIME HE FELT hate and anger was when he saw his mother crying for his uncle and his aunt. They both had caught tuberculosis and had been sent to different sanitariums. So, between the brothers and sisters, they had split up the children among themselves and had taken care of them as best they could. Then the aunt died, and soon thereafter they brought the uncle back from the sanitarium, but he was already spitting blood. That was when he saw his mother crying every little while. He became angry because he was unable to do anything against anyone. Today he felt the same. Only today it was for his father.

"You all should've come home right away, m'ijo. Couldn't you see that your Daddy was sick? You should have known that he'd suffered a sunstroke. Why didn't you come home?"

"I don't know. Us being so soaked with sweat, we didn't feel so hot, but I guess that when you're sunstruck it's different. But I did tell him to sit down under the tree that's at the edge of the rows, but he didn't want to. And that was when he started throwing up. Then we saw he couldn't hoe anymore and we dragged him and put him under a tree. He didn't put up a fuss at that point. He just let us take him. He didn't even say a word."

"Poor viejo, my poor viejo. Last night he hardly slept. Didn't you hear him outside the house. He squirmed in bed all night with cramps. God willing, he'll get well. I've been giving him cool lemonade all day, but his eyes still look glassy. If I'd gone to the fields yesterday, I tell you, he wouldn't have gotten sick. My poor viejo, he's going to have cramps all over his body for three days and three nights at the least. Now, you all take care of yourselves. Don't overwork yourselves so much. Don't pay any mind to that boss if he tries to rush you. Just don't do it. He thinks its so easy since he's not the one who's out there stooped."

He became even angrier when he heard his father moan outside the chicken coop. He wouldn't stay inside because he said it made him feel very anxious. Outside where he could feel the fresh air was where he got some relief. And also when the cramps came he could roll over on the grass. Then he thought about whether his father might die from the sunstroke. At times he heard his father start to pray and ask for God's help. At first he had faith that he would get well soon but by the next day he felt the anger growing of him. And all the more when he heard his mother and his father clamoring for God's mercy. That night, well past midnight, he had been awakened by his father's groans. His mother got up and removed the scapularies from around his neck and washed them. Then she lit some candles. But nothing happened. It was like his aunt and uncle all over again.

"What's to be gained from doing all that, Mother? Don't tell me you think it helped my aunt and uncle any. How come we're like this, like we're buried alive? Either the germs eat us alive or the sun burns us up. Always some kind of sickness. And every day we work and work. For what? Poor Dad, always working so hard. I think he was born working. Like he says, barely five years old and already helping his father plant corn. All the time feeding the earth and the sun, only to one day, just like that, get struck down by the sun. And there you are, helpless. And them, begging for God's help . . . why, God doesn't care about us . . . I don't think there even is . . . No, better not say it, what if Dad gets worse. Poor Dad, I guess that at least gives him some hope."

His mother noticed how furious he was, and that morning she told him to calm down, that everything was in God's hands and that with God's help his father was going to get well.

"Oh, Mother, do you really believe that? I am certain that God has no concern for us. Now you tell me, is Dad evil or mean-hearted? You tell me if he has ever done any harm to anyone."

"Of course not."

"So there you have it. You see? And my aunt and uncle? You explain. And the poor kids, now orphans, never having known their parents. Why did God have to take them away? I tell you, God could care less about the poor. Tell me, why must we live here like this? What have we done to deserve this? You're so good and yet you have to suffer so much."

"Oh, please, m'ijo, don't talk that way. Don't speak against the will of God. Don't talk that way, please, m'ijo. You scare me. It's as if already the blood of Satan runs through your veins."

"Well, maybe. That way at least, I could get rid of this anger. I'm so tired of thinking about it. Why? Why you? Why Dad? Why my uncle? Why my aunt? Why their kids? Tell me, Mother, why? Why us, burrowed in the dirt like animals with no hope for anything? You know the only hope we have is coming out here every year. And like you yourself say, only death brings rest. I think that's the way my aunt and uncle felt and that's how Dad must feel too."

"That's how it is, m'ijo. Only death brings us rest."

"But why us?"

"Well, they say that . . . "

"Don't say it. I know what you're going to tell me—that the poor go to heaven."

That day started out cloudy and he could feel the morning coolness brushing his eyelashes as he and his brothers and sisters began the day's labor. Their mother had to stay home to care for her husband. Thus, he felt responsible for hurrying on his brothers and sisters. During the morning, at least for the first few hours, they endured the heat but by ten-thirty the sun had suddenly cleared the skies and pressed down against the world. They began working more slowly because of the weakness, dizziness and suffocation they felt when they worked too fast. Then they had to wipe the sweat from their eyes every little while because their vision would get blurred.

"If you start blacking out, stop working, you hear me? Or go a little slower. When we reach the edge we'll rest a bit to get our strength back. It's gonna be hot today. If only it'd stay just a bit cloudy like this morning, then nobody would complain. But no, once the sun bears down like this not even one little cloud dares to appear out of fear. And the worst of it is we'll finish up here by two and then we have to go over to that other field that's nothing but hills. It's okay at the top of the hill but down in the lower part of the slopes it gets to be real suffocating. There's no breeze there. Hardly any air goes through. Remember?"

"Yeah."

"That's where the hottest part of the day will catch us. Just drink plenty of water every little while. It don't matter if the boss gets mad. Just don't get sick. And if you can't go on, tell me right away, all right? We'll go home. Y'all saw what happened to Dad when he pushed himself too hard. The sun has no mercy, it can eat you alive."

Just as they had figured, they had moved on to the other field by early afternoon. By three o'clock they were all soaked with sweat. Not one part of their clothing was dry. Every little while they would stop. At times they could barely breath, then they would black out and they would become fearful of getting sunstruck, but they kept on working.

"How do y'all feel?"

"Man, it's so hot! But we've got to keep on. 'Til six, at least. Except this water don't help our thirst any. Sure wish I had a bottle of cool water, real cool, fresh from the well, or a coke ice-cold."

"Are you crazy? That'd sure make you sunsick right now. Just don't work so fast. Let's see if we can make it until six. What do you think?"

At four o'clock the youngest became ill. He was only nine years old, but since he was paid the same as a grown up he tried to keep up with the rest. He began vomiting. He sat down, then he laid down. Terrified, the other children ran to where he lay and looked at him. It appeared that he had fainted and when they opened his eyelids they saw his eyes were rolled back. The next youngest child started crying but right away he told him to stop and help him carry his brother home. It seemed he was having cramps all over his little body. He lifted him and carried him by himself and, again, he began asking himself *why?*

"Why Dad and then my little brother? He's only nine years old. Why? He has to work like a mule buried in the earth. Dad, Mom, and my little brother here, what are they guilty of?"

Each step that he took towards the house resounded with the question, *why?* About halfway to the house he began to get furious. Then he started crying out of rage. His little brothers and sisters did not know what to do, and they, too, started crying, but out of fear. Then he started cursing. And without even realizing it, he said what he had been wanting to say for a long time. He cursed God. Upon doing this he felt that fear instilled in him by the years and by his parents. For a second he saw the earth opening up to devour him. Then he felt his footsteps against the earth, compact, more solid than ever. Then his anger swelled up again and he vented it by cursing God. He looked at his brother, he no longer looked sick. He didn't know whether his brothers and sisters had understood the graveness of his curse.

That night he did not fall asleep until very late. He felt at peace as never before. He felt as though he had become detached from everything. He no longer worried about his father nor his brother. All that he awaited was the new day, the freshness of the morning. By daybreak his father was doing better. He was on his way to recovery. And his little brother, too; the cramps had almost completely subsided. Frequently he felt a sense of surprise upon recalling what he had done the previous afternoon. He thought of telling his mother, but he decided to keep it secret. All he told her was that the earth did not devour anyone, nor did the sun.

He left for work and encountered a very cool morning. There were clouds in the sky and for the first time he felt capable of doing and undoing anything that he pleased. He looked down at the earth and kicked it hard and said.

"Not yet, you can't swallow me up yet. Someday, yes. But I'll never know it."

A STROKE LEFT THE GRANDFATHER PARALYZED from the neck down. One day one of his grandsons came by to visit with him. The grandfather asked him how old he was and what he most desired in life. The grandson replied that what he most wanted was for the next ten years to pass by immediately so that he would know what had happened in his life. The grandfather told him he was very stupid and cut off the conversation. The grandson did not understand why he had called him stupid until he turned thirty.

First Communion

T HE PRIEST ALWAYS HELD First Communion during mid-spring. I'll always remember that day in my life. I remember what I was wearing and I remember my godfather and the pastries and chocolate that we had after mass, but I also remember what I saw at the cleaners that was next to the church. I think it all happened because I left so early for church. It's that I hadn't been able to sleep the night before, trying to remember all of my sins, and worse yet, trying to arrive at an exact number. Furthermore, since Mother had placed a picture of hell at the head of the bed and since the walls of the room were papered with images of the devil and since I wanted salvation from all evil, that was all I could think of.

"Remember, children, very quiet, very very quiet. You have learned your prayers well, and now you know which are the mortal sins and which are the venial sins, now you know what sacrilege is, now you know that you are God's children, but you can also be children of the devil. When you go to confession you must tell all of your sins, you must try to remember all of the sins you have committed. Because if you forget one and receive Holy Communion then that would be a sacrilege and if you commit sacrilege you will go to hell. God knows all. You cannot lie to God. You can lie to me and to the priest, but God knows everything; so if your soul is not pure of sin, then you should not receive Holy Communion. That would be a sacrilege. So everyone confess all of your sins. Recall all of your sins. Wouldn't you be ashamed if you received Holy Communion and then later remembered a sin that you had forgotten to confess? Now, let's see, let us practice confessing our sins. Who would like to start off? Let us begin with the sins that we commit with our hands when we touch our bodies. Who would like to start?"

The nun liked for us to talk about the sins of the flesh. The real truth was that we practiced a lot telling our sins, but the real truth was that I didn't understand a lot of things. What did scare me was the idea of going to hell because some months earlier I had fallen against a small basin filled with hot coals which we used as a heater in the little room where we slept. I had burned my calf. I could well imagine how it might be to burn in hell forever. That was all that I understood. So I spent that night, the eve of my First Communion, going over all the sins I had committed. But what was real hard was coming up with the exact number like the nun wanted us to. It must have been dawn by the time I finally satisfied my conscience. I had committed one hundred and fifty sins, but I was going to admit to two-hundred.

"If I say one-hundred and fifty and I've forgotten some, that would be bad. I'll just say two-hundred and that way even if I forget lots of them I won't commit any kind of sacrilege. Yes, I have committed two-hundred sins . . . Father, I have come to confess my sins . . . How many? . . . Two-hundred . . . of all kinds . . . The Commandments? Against all of the Ten Commandments . . . This way there will be no sacrilege. It's better this way. By confessing more sins you'll be purer."

I remember I got up much earlier that morning than Mother had expected. My godfather would be waiting for me at the church and I didn't want to be even one second late.

"Hurry, Mother, get my pants ready, I thought you already ironed them last night."

"It's just that I couldn't see anymore last night. My eyesight is failing me now and that's why I had to leave them for this morning. But tell me, what's your hurry now? It's still very early. Confession isn't until eight o'clock and it's only six. Your padrino won't be there until eight."

"I know, but I couldn't sleep. Hurry, Mother, I want to leave now."

"And what are you going to do there so early?"

"Well, I want to leave because I'm afraid I'll forget the sins I have to confess to the priest. I can think better at the church."

"All right, I'll be through in just a minute. Believe me, as long as I can see I'm able to do a lot."

I headed for church repeating my sins and reciting the Holy Sacraments. The morning was already bright and clear but there weren't many people out in the street yet. The morning was cool. When I got to the church I found that it was closed. I think the priest might have overslept or was very busy. That was why I walked around the church and passed by the cleaners that was next to the church. The sound of loud laughter and moans surprised me because I didn't expect anybody to be in there. I thought it might be a dog but then it sounded like people again and that's why I peeked in through the little window in the door. They didn't see me but I saw them. They were naked and embracing each other, lying on some shirts and dresses on the floor. I don't know why but I couldn't move away from the window. Then they saw me and tried to cover themselves, and they yelled at me to get out of there. The woman's hair looked all messed up and she looked like she was sick. And me, to tell the truth, I got scared and ran to the church but I couldn't get my mind off of what I had seen. I realized then that maybe those were the sins that we committed with our hands. But I couldn't forget the sight of that woman and that man lying on the floor. When my friends started arriving I was going to tell them but then I thought it would be better to tell them after communion. More and more I was feeling like I was the one who had committed a sin of the flesh.

"There's nothing I can do now. But I can't tell the others 'cause they'll sin like me. I better not go to communion. Better that I don't go to confession. I can't, now that I know, I can't. But what will Mom and Dad say if I don't go to communion? And my padrino, I can't leave him there waiting. I have to confess what I saw. I feel like going back. Maybe they're still there on the floor. No choice, I'm gonna have to lie. What if I forget it between now and confession? Maybe I didn't see anything? And if I hadn't seen anything?"

I remember that when I went in to confess and the priest asked for my sins, all I told him was two-hundred and of all kinds. I did not confess the sin of the flesh. On returning to the house with my godfather, everything seemed changed, like I was and yet wasn't in the same place. Everything seemed smaller and less important. When I saw my Dad and my Mother, I imagined them on the floor. I started seeing all of the grown-ups naked and their faces even looked distorted, and I could even hear them laughing and moaning, even though they weren't even laughing. Then I started imagining the priest and the nun on the floor. I couldn't hardly eat any of the sweet bread or drink the chocolate. As soon as I finished, I recall running out of the house. It felt like I couldn't breath.

"So, what's the matter with him? Such manners!"
"Ah, compadre, let him be. You don't have to be concerned on my account. I have my own. These young ones, all they can think about is playing. Let him have a good time, it's the day of his First Communion."
"Sure, compadre, I'm not saying they shouldn't play. But they have to learn to be more courteous. They have to show more respect toward

adults, their elders, and all the more for their padrino."

"No, well, that's true."

I remember I headed toward the thicket. I picked up some rocks and threw them at the cactus. Then I broke some bottles. I climbed a tree and stayed there for a long time until I got tired of thinking. I kept remembering the scene at the cleaners, and there, alone, I even liked recalling it. I even forgot that I had lied to the priest. And then I felt the same as I once had when I had heard a missionary speak about the grace of God. I felt like knowing more about everything. And then it occurred to me that maybe everything was the same.

THE TEACHER WAS SURPRISED when, hearing that they needed a button on the poster to represent the button industry, the child tore one off his shirt and offered it to her. She was surprised because she knew that this was probably the only shirt the child had. She didn't know whether he did this to be helpful, to feel like he belonged or out of love for her. She did feel the intensity of the child's desire and this was what surprised her most of all.

The Little
Burnt Victims

THERE WERE FIVE IN THE GARCÍA FAMILY. Don Efraín, Doña Chona and their three children: Raulito, Juan and María—seven, six and five years old, respectively. On Sunday evening they arrived from the theater excited over the movie about boxing that they had seen. Don Efraín was the most excited. When they arrived, he brought out the boxing gloves he had bought for the children and then he made them put them on. He even stripped them down to their shorts and rubbed a bit of alcohol on their little chests, just like they had seen done in the movie. Doña Chona didn't like for them to box because someone would always end up getting mad and then the wailing would start and last for a long time.

"That's enough, viejo. Why do you make them fight? Remember how Juan's nose always starts to bleed and you know how hard it is to make the bleeding stop. Come on, viejo, let them go to bed."

"Man, vieja!"

"I'm not a man."

"Oh, let them fight. Maybe they'll at least learn how to defend themselves."

"But can't you see that we barely have enough room to stand up in this chicken shack and there you are running around like we had so much space."

"And what do you think they do when we go to work? I wish they were older so we could take them with us to the fields. They could work or at least sit quietly in the car."

"Yeah, but do you really think so? The older they get, the more restless they become. I don't like it at all leaving them here by themselves."

"Maybe one of them will turn out good with the glove, and then we'll be set vieja. Just think how much money champions win. Thousands and thousands. I'm gonna see if I can order them a punching bag through the catalog next week, as soon as we get paid."

"Well, true. You never know, right?"

"Right. That's what I'm telling you."

The three children were left to themselves in the house when they went to work because the owner didn't like children in the fields doing mischief and distracting their parents from their work. Once they took them along and kept them in the car, but the day had gotten very hot and suffocating and the children had even gotten sick. From then on they decided to leave them at home instead, although, sure enough, they worried about them all day long. Instead of packing a lunch, they went go home at noon to eat and that way they could check on them to see if they were all right. That following Monday they got up before dawn as usual and left for work. They left the children fast asleep.

"You look real happy, viejo."
"You know why."
"No, it's not just that. You look like you're happier than just because of that."
"It's just that I love my children so much, like you. And on the way I was thinking about how they also like to play with us."

At about ten o'clock that morning, from where they were working in the fields they noticed smoke rising from the direction of the farm. Everyone stopped working and ran to their cars. They sped toward the farm. When they arrived they found the Garcia's shack engulfed inflames. Only the eldest child was saved. The bodies of the other children were charred in the blaze.

"They say that the oldest child made little Juan and María put on the gloves. They were just playing. But then I think he rubbed some alcohol on their chests and who knows what other stuff on their little bodies like they had seen done in the movie. That's how they were playing."
"But how did the fire get started?"
"Well, poor things, the oldest, Raulito, started to fry some eggs while they were playing and somehow or other their little bodies caught on fire, and you can imagine."
"He must have rubbed lots of alcohol on them."
"You know all the junk that piles up in the house, so cramped for space and all. I believe the kerosene tank on the stove exploded and . . . that was it. The explosion must have covered them with flames and, of course, the shack, too."
"Why, sure."

"And you know what?"

"What?"

"The only thing that didn't get burnt up was the pair of gloves. They say they found the little girl all burnt up and with the gloves on."

"But I wonder why the gloves didn't get burned up?"

"Well, you know how those people can make things so good. Not even fire can destroy them."

"And the García's, how are they getting along?"

"Well, they're getting over their grief, although I don't believe they'll ever be able to forget it. What else can you do? I tell you, you never know when your turn's up. My heart goes out to them. But you never know."

"So true."

IT WAS A BEAUTIFUL WEDDING DAY. Throughout the entire week prior the groom and his father had been busy fixing up the yard at the bride's house and setting up a canvass tent where the couple would receive the congratulations of family and friends. For decorations they used the limbs of pecan trees and wild flowers and everything was arranged very nicely. Then they smoothed down the ground in front of the tent very neatly. Every little while they sprinkled water on it to pack down the soil. This way the dust wouldn't get stirred up so much once the dancing got started. After they were married in the church the couple strolled down the street followed by a procession of godmothers and godfathers and ahead of them a bunch of children running and shouting, "Here come the newlyweds!"

The Night the Lights Went Out

THE NIGHT THE LIGHTS of the town went out some became frightened and others did not. It wasn't storming nor was there any lightning, so some didn't find out until later. Those who were at the dance had found out but those who weren't hadn't . . . until the next day. Those who stayed home just noticed that right after the lights went out the music was no longer heard through the night and they figured that the dance had ended. But they didn't find out anything until the next day.

"That Ramón, he loved his girlfriend a lot. Yes, he loved her a lot. I know so because he was my friend and, well, you know he wasn't one who talked much, but anyway, he would tell me everything. Many times he'd say how much he loved her. They'd been going together since last year and they had given each other real pretty rings that they bought at Kress. And she loved him too but who knows what had happened this summer. They say it was the first time in four months that he had seen her . . . no one knows, no one really knows . . . "

"Look, I promise you I'm not gonna see anybody else or flirt with anyone. I promise you. I want to marry you . . . Look, we can go away together right now if you want to . . . Well, we'll wait then, until we finish school. But, look, I promise you I won't go around with anyone else nor flirt with anyone. I promise you. We can leave right now if you want to. I can support you. I know, I know . . . but they'll get over it. Let's go. Will you go with me?"

"No, it's better to wait, don't you think? It's better if we do it right. I promise you too . . . You know that I love you. Trust me. Dad wants me to finish school. And, well, I have to do what he says. But that doesn't mean I don't love you just 'cause I can't go away with you. I do love you, I love you very much. I won't go around with anybody else either. I promise you."

"Oh, come on. You know everybody knows. I heard something else. Somebody told me that she'd been going around with some dude out there in Minnesota. And that she still kept on writing to Ramón. Kept on lying to him. Some of Ramón's friends told him everything. They were working at the same farm where she was.

And then when they saw him out here they told him right off. He was faithful to her but she wasn't. She was going around with some guy from San Antonio. He was nothing but a show-off and he was always all duded up. They say he wore orange shoes and real long coats and always had his collar turned up . . . But her, I think she liked to mess around, otherwise she wouldn't have been unfaithful. What was bad was her not breaking up with him. When he found out, Juanita hadn't returned yet from up north and he took to drinking a lot. I saw him once when he was drunk and all he would say was that he was hurting. That that was all that women left behind, nothing but pain inside."

"When I get back to Texas I'll take her away with me. I can't go on like this anymore. She'll come with me. She will. She's done me wrong. How I love her. With each swing of this hoe I hear her name. How come you feel this way when you're in love? I no sooner finish supper and I'm staring at her picture until dark. And at noon, during the lunch hour, too. But the thing is, I don't really remember how she looks. The picture doesn't seem to look like her anymore. Or she doesn't look like the picture. When the others make fun of me, I just go off to the woods. I see the picture but I just don't remember anymore how she looks, even if I see her picture. Maybe it's best to not look at it so much. She promised she'd be faithful. And she is, because her eyes and her smile keep telling me so when I picture her in my mind. Soon it'll be time to return to Texas. Each time I wake to the early crow of the roosters I feel like I'm already there and that I'm watching her walk down the street. It won't be long now."

"Well, it's not that I don't love Ramón, but this guy, he's a real smooth talker and we just talk, that's all. And all the girls just stare at him. He dresses really fine, too. It's not that I don't love Ramón, but this guy is real nice and his smile, I see it all day long . . . No, I'm not breaking up with Ramón. And, anyway, what's wrong with just talking? I don't want to get serious with this guy, I promised Ramón . . . but he just keeps on following and following me around. I don't want to get serious with him . . . I don't want to lose Ramón, I'm not getting involved with this guy. I just want him around to make the other girls jealous. No, I can't break up with Ramón because I really do love him a lot. It won't be long before we'll see each other again . . . Who said he was talking to Petra? Well, then, why is he always following me around? I'll have you know he even sends me letters every day with Don José's little boy."

" . . . I know you're going with someone else but I like talking to you. Since I got here and saw you I want to be with you more and more. Go to the dance Saturday and dance with me all night . . . Love you, Ramiro."

"They say she danced the whole night with Ramiro. I think her friends told her something about it but she just ignored them. This happened about the time when the work season was almost over and at the last dance, when they were saying good-bye, they promised to see each other back here. I don't think she even remembered Ramón at that moment. But by then Ramón already knew everything. That's why on that day, after not seeing each other in four months, he threw it all in her face. I was with him that day, I was with him when he saw her and I remember well that he was so happy to see her that he wasn't mad anymore. But then, after talking to her for a while he started getting mad all over again. They broke up right then and there."

"You do whatever you want."
"You can be sure of that."
"You're breaking up with me?"
"Yeah, and if you go to the dance tonight you better not dance with anyone else."
"And why shouldn't I? We're not going around anymore. We broke up. You can't tell me what to do."
"I don't care if we broke up or not. You're gonna pay for this. You're gonna do what I say, when I say and for as long as I say. Nobody makes a fool out of me. You're gonna pay for this one, one way or another."
"You can't tell me what to do."
"You're gonna do what I say and if you don't dance with me, you don't dance with anyone. And I mean for the entire dance."

"Well, they say that Juanita asked her parents for permission to leave early for the dance. She went with some of her friends and the orchestra hadn't even started playing yet and there they were already at the dance hall, standing by the door so the guys would see them and ask them to dance right away. Juanita had been dancing with only one guy when Ramón got there. He walked in and looked all around for her. He saw her dancing and when the song ended he went over and grabbed her away from the guy. This guy, just a kid, didn't say anything, he just walked away and asked someone else to dance. Anyway, when the music started again Juanita refused to dance with Ramón. They were standing right in the middle of the dance floor and all the other couples were dancing around them. They stood there arguing and then she slapped him, and he yelled something at her and charged out of the dance hall. Juanita walked over to a bench and sat down. The song hadn't even ended when all the lights went out. There was a bunch of yelling and screaming and they tried to turn them back on but then they saw that the whole town had blacked out."

The workers from the light company found Ramón inside the power plant that was about a block away from the dance hall. They say that his body was burnt to a crisp and that he was holding on to one of the transformers. That's why all the lights of the town went out. The people at the dance found out almost right away. And the ones who were close to Ramón and Juanita heard him tell her that he was going to kill himself because of her. The people at home didn't find out until the next day, that Sunday morning before and after mass.

> "They just loved each other so much, don't you think?"
> "No doubt."

A LITTLE BEFORE SIX, just before the spinach pickers would be getting home, there was the high-pitched signal of the horn at the water tank then the sound of fire trucks, and then some moments later the ambulance sirens. By six o'clock some of the workers arrived with the news of how one of the trucks transporting workers had collided with a car and was still burning. When the car hit it, those who were not thrown out of the van on impact were trapped. Those who witnessed the crash said that the truck had immediately burst into flames and that they had seen some victims, poor souls, running from the wreckage toward the thicket with their hair aflame. They say the Anglo woman driving the car was from a dry county and that she'd been at a bar drinking, upset because her husband had left her. There were sixteen dead.

The
Night Before
Christmas

CHRISTMAS EVE was approaching and the barrage of commercials, music and Christmas cheer over the radio and the blare of announcements over the loud speakers on top of the stationwagon advertising movies at the Teatro Ideal resounded and seemed to draw it closer. It was three days before Christmas when Doña María decided to buy something for her children. This was the first time she would buy them toys. Every year she intended to do it but she always ended up facing up to the fact that, no, they couldn't afford it. She knew that her husband would be bringing each of the children candies and nuts anyway and, so she would rationalize that they didn't need to get them anything else. Nevertheless, every Christmas the children asked for toys. She always appeased them with the same promise. She would tell them to wait until the sixth of January, the day of the Magi, and by the time that day arrived the children had already forgotten all about it. But now she was noticing that each year the children seemed less and less taken with Don Chon's visit on Christmas Eve when he came bearing a sack of oranges and nuts.

"But why doesn't Santa Claus bring us anything?"

"What do you mean? What about the oranges and nuts he brings you?"

"No, that's Don Chon."

"No, I'm talking about what you always find under the sewing machine."

"What, Dad's the one who brings that, don't think we don't know that. Aren't we good like the other kids?"

"Of course, you're good children. Why don't you wait until the day of the Reyes Magos. That's when toys and gifts really arrive. In Mexico, it's not Santa Claus who brings gifts, but the Three Wisemen. And they don't come until the sixth of January. That's the real date."

"Yeah, but they always forget. They've never brought us anything, not on Christmas Eve, not on the day of the Three Kings."

"Well, maybe this time they will."

"Yeah, well, I sure hope so."

That was why she made up her mind to buy them something. But they didn't have the money to spend on toys. Her husband worked almost eighteen hours a day washing dishes and cooking at a restaurant. He didn't have time to go downtown and buy toys. Besides, they had to save money every week to pay for the trip up north. Now they even charged for children too, even if they rode standing up the whole way to Iowa. So it cost them a lot to make the trip. In any case, that night when her husband arrived, tired from work, she talked to him about getting something for the children.

"Look, viejo, the children want something for Christmas."

"What about the oranges and nuts I bring them."

"Well, they want toys. They're not content anymore with just fruits and nuts. They're a little older now and more aware of things."

"They don't need anything."

"Now, you can't tell me you didn't have toys when you were a kid."

"I used to *make* my own toys, out of clay . . . little horses and little soldiers . . . "

"Yes, but it's different here. They see so many things . . . come on, let's go get them something . . . I'll go to Kress myself."

"You?"

"Yes, me."

"Aren't you afraid to go downtown? You remember that time in Wilmar, out in Minnesota, how you got lost downtown. Are you sure you're not afraid?"

"Yes, yes, I remember, but I'll just have to get my courage up. I've thought about it all day long and I've set my mind to it. I'm sure I won't get lost here. Look, I go out to the street. From here you can see the ice house. It's only four blocks away, so Doña Regina tells me. When I get to the ice house I turn to the right and go two blocks and there's downtown. Kress is right there. Then, I come out of Kress, walk back towards the ice house and turn back on this street, and here I am."

"I guess it really won't be difficult. Yeah. Fine. I'll leave you some money on top of the table when I go to work in the morning. But be careful, vieja, there's a lot of people downtown these days."

The fact was that Doña María very rarely left the house. The only time she did was when she visited her father and her sister who lived on the next block. And she only went to church whenever someone died and, occasionally, when there was a wedding. But she went with her husband, so she never took notice of where she was going. And her husband always brought her everything. He was the one who bought the groceries and clothing. In reality she was unfamiliar with downtown even though it was only six blocks away. The cemetery was on the other side of downtown and the church was also in that direction. The only time that they passed through downtown was whenever they were on their way to San Antonio or whenever they were returning from up north. And this would usually be during the wee hours of the morning or at night. But that day she was determined and she started making preparations.

The next day she got up early as usual, and after seeing her husband and children off, she took the money from the table and began getting ready to go downtown. This didn't take her long.

"My God, I don't know why I'm so fearful. Why, downtown is only six blocks from here. I just go straight and then after I cross the tracks turn right. Then go two blocks and there's Kress. On the way back, I walk two blocks back and then I turn to the left and keep walking until I'm home again. God willing, there won't be any dogs on the way. And I just pray that the train doesn't come while I'm crossing the tracks and catches me right in the middle . . . I just hope there's no dogs . . . I hope there's no train coming down the tracks."

She walked the distance from the house to the railroad tracks rapidly. She walked down the middle of the street all the way. She was afraid to walk on the sidewalk. She feared she might get bitten by a dog or that someone might grab her. In actuality there was only one dog along the entire stretch and most of the people didn't even notice her walking toward downtown. She nevertheless kept walking down the middle of the street and, luckily, not a single car passed by, otherwise she would not have known what to do. Upon arriving at the crossing she was suddenly struck by intense fear. She could hear the sound of moving trains and their whistles blowing and this was unnerving her. She was too scared to cross. Each time she mustered enough courage to cross she heard the whistle of the train and, frightened, she retreated and ended up at the same place. Finally, overcoming her fear, she shut her eyes and crossed the tracks. Once she got past the tracks, her fear began to subside. She got to the corner and turned to the right.

The sidewalks were crowded with people and her ears started to fill up with a ringing sound, the kind that, once it started, it wouldn't stop. She didn't recognize any of the people around her. She wanted to turn back but she was caught in the flow of the crowd which shoved her onward toward downtown and the sound kept ringing louder and louder in her ears. She became frightened and more and more she was finding herself unable to remember why she was there amidst the crowd of people. She stopped in an alley way between two stores to regain her composure a bit. She stood there for a while watching the passing crowd.

> "My God, what is happening to me? I'm starting to feel the same way I did in Wilmar. I hope I don't get worse. Let me see . . . the ice house is in that direction—no it's that way. No, my God, what's happening to me? Let me see . . . I came from over there to here. So it's in that direction. I should have just stayed home. Uh, can you tell me where Kress is, please? . . . Thank you."

She walked to where they had pointed and entered the store. The noise and pushing of the crowd was worse inside. Her anxiety soared. All she wanted was to leave the store but she couldn't find the doors anywhere, only stacks and stacks of merchandise and people crowded against one another. She even started hearing voices coming from the merchandise. For a while she stood, gazing blankly at what was in front of her. She couldn't even remember the names of the things. Some people stared at her for a few seconds, others just pushed her aside. She remained in this state for a while, then she started walking again. She finally made out some toys and put them in her bag. Then she saw a wallet and also put that in her bag. Suddenly she no longer heard the noise of the crowd. She only saw the people moving about—their legs, their arms, their mouths, their eyes. She finally asked where the door, the exit was. They told her and she started in that direction. She pressed through the crowd, pushing her way until she pushed open the door and exited.

She had been standing on the sidewalk for only a few seconds, trying to figure out where she was, when she felt someone grab her roughly by the arm. She was grabbed so tightly that she gave out a cry.

> "Here she is . . . these damn people, always stealing something, stealing. I've been watching you all along. Let's have that bag."
> "But . . . "

Then she heard nothing for a long time. All she saw was the pavement moving swiftly toward her face and a small pebble that bounced into her eye and was hurting a lot. She felt someone pulling her arms and when they turned her, face up, all she saw were faces far away. Then she saw a security guard with a gun in his holster and she was terrified. In that instant she thought about her children and her eyes filled with tears. She started crying. Then she lost consciousness of what was happening around her, only feeling herself drifting in a sea of people, their arms brushing against her like waves.

"It's a good thing my compadre happened to be there. He's the one who ran to the restaurant to tell me. How do you feel?"

"I think I must be insane, viejo."

"That's why I asked you if you weren't afraid you might get sick like in Wilmar."

"What will become of my children with a mother who's insane? A crazy woman who can't even talk, can't even go downtown."

"Anyway, I went and got the notary public. He's the one who went with me to the jail. He explained everything to the official. That you got dizzy and that you get nervous attacks whenever you're in a crowd of people."

"And if they send me to the insane asylum? I don't want to leave my children. Please, viejo, don't let them take me, don't let them. I shouldn't have gone downtown."

"Just stay here inside the house and don't leave the yard. There's no need for it anyway. I'll bring you everything you need. Look, don't cry anymore, don't cry. No, go ahead and cry, it'll make you feel better. I'm gonna talk to the kids and tell them to stop bothering you about Santa Claus. I'm gonna tell them there's no Santa Claus, that way they won't trouble you with that anymore."

"No, viejo, don't be mean. Tell them that if he doesn't bring them anything on Christmas Eve, it's because the Reyes Magos will be bringing them something."

"But . . . well, all right, whatever you say. I suppose it's always best to have hope."

The children, who were hiding behind the door, heard everything, but they didn't quite understand it all. They awaited the day of the Reyes Magos as they did every year. When that day came and went with no arrival of gifts, they didn't ask for explanations.

BEFORE PEOPLE LEFT FOR UP NORTH the priest would bless their cars and trucks at five dollars each. One time he made enough money to take a trip to Barcelona, in Spain, to visit his parents and friends. He brought back words of gratitude from his family and some postcards of a very modern church. These he placed by the entrance of the church for the people to see, that they might desire a church such as that one. It wasn't long before words began to appear on the cards, then crosses, lines, and con safos symbols, just as had happened to the new church pews. The priest was never able to understand the sacrilege.

The Portrait

As soon as the people returned from up north the portrait salesmen began arriving from San Antonio. They would come to rake in. They knew that the workers had money and that was why, as Dad used to say, they would flock in. They carried suitcases packed with samples and always wore white shirts and ties. That way they looked more important and the people believed everything they would tell them and invite them into their homes without giving it much thought. I think that down deep they even longed for their children to one day be like them. In any event, they would arrive and make their way down the dusty streets, going house to house carrying suitcases full of samples.

I remember once I was at the house of one of my father's friends when one of these salesmen arrived. I also remember that that particular one seemed a little frightened and timid. Don Mateo asked him to come in because he wanted to do business.

"Good afternoon, traveler. I would like to tell you about something new that we're offering this year."

"Well, let's see, let's see . . . "

"Well, Sir, see, you give us a picture, any picture you may have, and we will not only enlarge it for you but we'll also set it in a wooden frame like this one and with inlays, like this—three dimensional, as they say."

"And what for?"

"So that it will look real. That way . . . look, let me show you . . . see? Doesn't he look real, like he's alive?"

"Man, he sure does. Look, vieja. This looks great. Well, you know, we wanted to send some pictures to be enlarged . . . but now, this must cost a lot, right?"

"No, I'll tell you, it costs about the same. Of course, it takes more time."

"Well, tell me, how much?"

'For as little as thirty dollars we'll deliver it to you done with inlays just like this, one this size."

"Boy, that's expensive! Didn't you say it didn't cost a lot more? Do you take installments?"

"Well, I'll tell you, we have a new manager and he wants everything in cash. It's very fine work. We'll make it look like real. Done like that, with inlays . . . take a look. What do you think? Some fine work, wouldn't you say? We can have it all finished for you in a month. You just tell us what color you want the clothes to be and we'll come by with it all finished one day when you least expect, framed and all. Yes, sir, a month at the longest. But like I say, this man who's the new manager, he wants the full payment in cash. He's very demanding, even with us."

"Yes, but it's much too expensive."

"Well, yes. But the thing is, this is very fine work. You can't say you've ever seen portraits done like this, with wood inlays."

"No, well, that's true. What do you think, vieja?"

"Well, I like it a lot. Why don't we order one? And if it turns out good . . . my Chuy . . . may he rest in peace. It's the only picture we have of him. We took it right before he left for Korea. Poor m'ijo, we never saw him again. See . . . this is his picture. Do you think you can make it like that, make it look like he's alive?"

"Sure, we can. You know, we've done a lot of them in soldier's uniforms and shaped it, like you see in this sample, with inlays. Why, it's more than just a portrait. Sure. You just tell me what size you want and whether you want a round or square frame. What do you say? How should I write it down?"

"What do you say, vieja, should we have it done like this one?"

"Well, I've already told you what I think. I would like to have m'ijo's picture fixed up like that and in color."

"All right, go ahead and write it down. But you take good care of that picture for us because it's the only one we have of our son grown up. He was going to send us one all dressed up in uniform with the American and Mexican flags crossed over his head, but he no sooner got there when a letter arrived telling us that he was lost in action. So you take good care of it."

"Don't you worry. We're responsible people. And we understand the sacrifices that you people make. Don't worry. And you just wait and see. When we bring it to you'll see how pretty it's gonna look. What do you say, should we make the uniform navy blue?"

"But he's not wearing a uniform in that picture."

"No, but that's just a matter of fixing it up with some wood fiber overlays. Look at these. This one, he didn't have a uniform on but we put one on him. So what do you say? Should we make it navy blue?"

"All right."

"Don't you worry about the picture."

And that was how they spent the entire day going house to house, street by street, their suitcases stuffed with pictures. As it turned out, a whole lot of people had ordered enlargements of that kind.

"They should be delivering those portraits soon, don't you think?"

"I think so, it's delicate work and takes more time. That's some fine work those people do. Did you see how real those pictures looked?"

"Yeah, sure. They do some fine work. You can't deny that. But it's already been over a month since they passed by here."

"Yes, but from here they went on through all the towns picking up pictures . . . all the way to San Antonio for sure. So it'll probably take a little longer."

"That's true, that's true."

And two more weeks had passed by the time they made the discovery. Some very heavy rains had come and some children who were playing in one of the tunnels leading to the dump found a sack full of pictures, all wormeaten and soaking wet. The only reason they could tell that these were pictures was because there were a lot of them and most of them the same size and with faces that could just barely be made out. Everybody caught on right away. Don Mateo was so angry that he took off to San Antonio to find the so and so who had swindled them.

"Well, you know, I stayed at Esteban's house. And every day I went with him to the market to sell produce. I helped him with everything. I had faith that I would run into that son of a gun some day soon. Then, after I'd been there for a few days, I started going out to the different barrios and I found out a lot that way. It wasn't so much the money that upset me. It was my poor vieja, crying and all because we'd lost the only picture we had of Chuy. We found it in the sack with all the other pictures but it was already ruined, you know."

"I see, but tell me, how did you find him?"

"Well, you see, to make a long story short, he came by the stand at the market one day. He stood right in front of us and bought some vegetables. It was like he was trying to remember who I was. Of course, I recognized him right off. Because when you're angry enough, you don't forget a face. I just grabbed him right then and there. Poor guy couldn't even talk. He was all scared. And I told him that I wanted that portrait of my son and that I wanted it three dimensional and that he'd best get it for me or I'd let him have it."

And I went with him to where he lived. And I put him to work right then and there. The poor guy didn't know where to begin. He had to do it all from memory."

"And how did he do it?"

"I don't know. I suppose if you're scared enough, you're capable of doing anything. Three days later he brought me the portrait all finished, just like you see it there on that table by the Virgin Mary. Now tell me, how do you like the way my boy looks?"

"Well, to be honest, I don't remember too well how Chuy looked. But he was beginning to look more and more like you, isn't that so?"

"Yes, I would say so. That's what everybody tells me now. That Chuy's a chip off the old block and that he was already looking like me. There's the portrait. Like they say, one and the same."

T HEY LET FIGUEROA OUT. He's been out a week."

"Yeah, but he's not well. There in the pen, if they don't like someone, they'll give them injections so they'll die."

"Damn right. Who do you think turned him in?"

"Probably some gringo who couldn't stand seeing him in town with that white girl he brought back with him from Wisconsin. And no one to defend him. They say the little gringa was seventeen and it's against the law."

"I'll bet you he won't last a year."

"Well, they say he has a very strange disease."

When We Arrive

AT ABOUT FOUR O'CLOCK in the morning the truck broke down. All night they stood hypnotized by the high-pitched whir of the tires turning against the pavement. When the truck stopped they awakened. The silence alone told them something was wrong. All along the way the truck had been overheating and then when they stopped and checked the motor they saw that it had practically burned up. It just wouldn't go anymore. They would have to wait there until daybreak and then ask for a lift to the next town. Inside the trailer the people awakened and then struck up several conversations. Then in the darkness their eyes had gradually begun to close and all became so silent that all that could be heard was the chirping of the crickets. Some were sleeping, others were thinking.

"Good thing the truck stopped here. My stomach's been hurting a lot for some time but I would've had to wake up a lot of people to get to the window and ask them to stop. But you still can't hardly see anything. Well, I'm getting off, see if I can find a field or a ditch. Must've been that chile I ate, it was so hot but I hated to let it go to waste. I hope my vieja is doing all right in there, carrying the baby and all."

"This driver that we have this year is a good one. He keeps on going. He doesn't stop for anything. Just gases up and let's go. We've been on the road over twenty-four hours. We should be close to Des Moines. Sure wish I could sit down for just a little while at least. I'd get out and lie down on the side of the road but there's no telling if there's snakes or some other kind of animal. Just before I fell asleep on my feet it felt like my knees were going to buckle. But I guess your body gets used to it right away 'cause it doesn't seem so hard anymore. But the kids must feel real tired standing like this all the way and with nothing to hold on to. Us grownups can at least hold on to this center bar that supports the canvas. And to think we're not as crowded as other times. I think there must be forty of us at the most. I remember that one time I traveled with that bunch of wetbacks, there were more than sixty of us.

We couldn't even smoke."

"What a stupid woman! How could she be so dumb as to throw that diaper out the front of the truck. It came sliding along the canvas and good thing I had glasses on or I would even have gotten the shit in my eyes! What a stupid woman! How could she do that? She should've known that crap would be blown towards all of us standing up back here. Why the hell couldn't she just wait until we got to a gas station and dump the shit there!"

"El Negrito just stood there in disbelief when I ordered the fifty-four hamburgers. At two in the morning. And since I walked into the restaurant alone and I'm sure he didn't see the truck pull up loaded with people. His eyes just popped wide open . . . 'at two o'clock in the morning, hamburgers? Fifty-four of them? Man, you must eat one hell of a lot.' It's that the people hadn't eaten and the driver asked for just one of us to get out and order for everyone. El Negrito was astounded. He couldn't believe what I ordered, that I wanted fifty-four hamburgers. At two o'clock in the morning you can eat that many hamburgers very easily, especially when you're starving."

". . . As soon as we get to the farm I'm getting the hell out. I'll go look for a job in Minneapolis. I'll be damned if I go back to Texas. Out here you can at least make a living at a decent job. I'll look for my uncle, see if he can find me a job at the hotel where he works as a bell-boy. Who knows, maybe they'll give me a break there or at some other hotel. And then the gringas, that's just a matter of finding them."

"If things go well this year, maybe we'll buy us a car so we won't have to travel this way, like cattle. The girls are pretty big now and I know they feel embarrassed. Sometimes they have some good buys at the gas stations out there. I'll talk to my compadre, he knows some of the car salesmen. I'll get one I like, even if it's old. I'm tired of coming out here in a truck like this. My compadre drove back a good little car last year. If we do well with the onion crop, I'll buy me one that's at least half-way decent. I'll teach my boy how to drive and he can take it all the way to Texas. As long as he doesn't get lost like my nephew. They didn't stop to ask for directions and ended up in New Mexico instead of Texas. Or I'll get Mundo to drive it and I won't charge him for gas. I'll see if he wants to."

"With the money Mr. Thompson loaned me we have enough to

buy food for at least two months. By then we should have the money from the beet crop. Just hope we don't get too much in debt. He loaned me two-hundred dollars but by the time you pay for the trip practically half of it is gone, and now that they've started charging me half-fare for the children . . . And then when we return, I have to pay him back double. Four-hundred dollars. That's too much interest, but what can you do? When you need it, you need it. Some people have told me to report him because that's way too much interest but now he's even got the deed to the house. I'm just hoping that things go okay for us with the beet crop or else we'll be left to the wind, home-less. We have to save enough to pay him back the four-hundred. And then we'll see if we have something left. And these kids, they need to start going to school. I don't know. I hope it goes okay for us, if not I don't know how we're going to do it. I just pray to God that there's work. . . ."

"Poor viejo. He must be real tired now, standing up the whole trip. I saw him nodding off a little while ago. And with no way to help him, what with these two in my arms. How I wish we were there already so we could lie down, even if it's on the hard floor. These children are nothing but trouble. I hope I'll be able to help him out in the fields, but I'm afraid that this year, what with these kids, I won't be able to do anything. I have to breastfeed them every little while and then they're still so little. If only they were just a bit older. I'm still going to try my best to help him out. At least along his row so he won't feel so over-worked. Even if it's just for short whiles. My poor viejo . . . the children are still so little and already he wishes they could start school. I just hope I'll be able to help him. God willing, I'll be able to help him."

"What a great view of the stars from here! It looks like they're coming down and touching the tarp of the truck. It's almost like there aren't any people inside. There's hardly any traffic at this hour. Every now and then a trailer passes by. The silence of the morning twilight makes everything look like it's made of satin. And now, what do I wipe myself with? Why couldn't it always be early dawn like this? We're going to be here till midday for sure. By the time they find help in the town and then by the time they fix the motor . . . If only it could stay like early dawn, then nobody would complain. I'm going to keep my eyes on the stars till the last one disappears. I wonder how many more people are watching the same star? And how many more might there be wondering how many are looking at the same star? It's so silent it looks like it's the stars the crickets are calling to."

"Goddamn truck. It's nothing but trouble. When we get there everybody will just have to look out for themselves. All I'm doing is dropping them off with the growers and I'm getting the hell out. Besides, we don't have a contract. They'll find themselves somebody to take them back to Texas. Somebody's bound to come by and pick them up. You can't make money off beets anymore. My best bet is to head back to Texas just as soon as I drop these people off and then see how things go hauling watermelons. The melon season's almost here. All I need now is for there not to be anyone in this goddamn town who can fix the truck. What the hell will I do then? So long as the cops don't come by and start hassling me about moving the truck from here. Boy, that town had to be the worst. We didn't even stop and still the cop caught up with us just to tell us that he didn't want us staying there. I guess he just wanted to show off in front of the town people. But we didn't even stop in their goddamn town. When we get there, as soon as I drop them off, I'll turn back. Each one to fend for himself."

"When we get there I'm gonna see about getting a good bed for my vieja. Her kidneys are really bothering her a lot nowadays. just hope we don't end up in a chicken coop like last year, with that cement floor. Even though you cover it with straw, once the cold season sets in you just can't stand it. That was why my rheumatism got so bad, I'm sure of that."

"When we arrive, when we arrive, the real truth is that I'm tired of arriving. Arriving and leaving, it's the same thing because we no sooner arrive and . . . the real truth of the matter . . . I'm tired of arriving. I really should say when we don't arrive because that's the real truth. We never arrive."

"When we arrive, when we arrive. . . "

Little by little the crickets ceased their chirping. It seemed as though they were becoming tired and the dawn gradually affirmed the presence of objects; ever so carefully and very slowly, so that no one would take notice of what was happening. And the people were becoming people. They began getting out of the trailer and they huddled around and commenced to talk about what they would do when they arrived.

BARTOLO PASSED THROUGH town every December when he knew that most of the people had returned from work up north. He always came by selling his poems. By the end of the first day, they were almost sold out because the names of the people of the town appeared in the poems. And when he read them aloud it was something emotional and serious. I recall that one time he told the people to read the poems out loud because the spoken word was the seed of love in the darkness.

Under
the House

THE FLEAS MADE him move. He was under a house. He had been there for several hours, or so it seemed to him, hiding. That morning on his way to school he felt the urge not to go. He thought of how the teacher would spank him for sure because he didn't know the words. Then he thought of crawling under the house but not just because of that. He felt like hiding, too, but he didn't know where nor for how long, so he just went ahead and hid there. At first the fleas didn't bother him and he felt very comfortable in the dark. Although he was sure there were spiders, he had crawled in unafraid and there he remained. From where he was all he could make out was a white strip of daylight, about a foot high, lining the house all around. He was lying face down and whenever he moved he could feel his back brush against the floor of the house. This even gave him a feeling of secu-rity. But once the fleas started biting him he had to move constantly. And he started to worry that the people who lived there might find out that he was there and make him get out. But he had to keep moving constantly.

> *I wonder how long I've been here now. The kids came out of the house to play some time ago. It seems I've been here for a good while. As long as they don't look under the house 'cause they'll see me for sure, and then what? The children look funny, all I can see are their legs running. It's not bad here. I could come here every day. I think that must be what the others do when they play hooky. No one to bother me here. I can think in peace.*

He had even forgotten all about the fleas and even that he was under the house. He could think very clearly in the dark. He didn't need to close his eyes. He thought about his father for a while, about how he used to tell him stories at night about witches and how he would make them fall from the sky by praying and tying the seven knots.

> *When I'd be coming back from work, at that time we had our own land with irrigation, in the early morning twilight, I'd always see these globes of light, like fireballs, bouncing off the telephone lines. They would come from*

the direction of Morelos, they say that's where they originate. One time I nearly made one fall down. Don Remigio taught me how to say the seven prayers that go with the seven knots. All you have to do is start praying when you see those balls of fire. After each prayer you tie a knot. This one time I got to the seventh prayer but you know, I wasn't able to tie that last knot, but the witch fell anyway, practically landing at my feet, and then she got up . . . The boy was so young and children don't understand too much at that age. And he couldn't hold out. They're not going to do anything to the boss, he's got too much pull. Can you imagine what they'd do if one of us killed one of their kids? They say that one day the boy's father took a rifle and went looking for him because he wanted to pay him back but he didn't find him . . . The woman would almost always start crying when she entered the church, and then she'd start praying. But before she was even aware of it, she would start talking in a loud voice. Then she'd start yelling, like she was having some kind of attack . . . I think Doña Cuquita is still living. I haven't seen her in a long time. She used to be very careful whenever we went to the dump. Now her I really loved. And since I never knew my grandparents. I think even Dad loved her like a grandmother because he, too, never knew his grandparents. What I liked best was for her to embrace me and tell me, "You're smarter than an eagle and more watchful than the moon" . . . Get out of there! Get away from that goddamn window! Go away! Go away . . . You know, you can't come home with me anymore. Look, I don't mind playing with you but some old ladies told mama that Mexicans steal and now mama says not to bring you home anymore. You have to turn back. But we can still play at school. I'll choose you and you choose me . . . What can I tell you! I know what I'm telling you, I'm saying that we can't get any more screwed than we already are. I know why I'm telling you. If there's another war, we won't be the ones to suffer. Don't be a damn fool. The ones who will pay for it are the ones on top, the ones who have something. Us, we're already screwed. If there's another war, hell, things might even get better for us . . . Why don't you eat sweetbread anymore? You don't like it, anymore? . . . Well, I tell you, I even went downtown and bought me a new hammer so I could be ready for when they'd come to teach us. They say that the minister, when he found out, he went straight home, took a hatchet and broke all the furniture to pieces and than he took everything outside and set it on fire. He stood there and watched everything burn to ashes . . . I don't think my viejo is going to be able to work out in the sun anymore. The boss didn't say a thing when we told him that he had gotten sick from the heat. He just shook his head. What worried him the most was that it was raining too much and the crop was getting ruined. That was the only thing he was sad about. He wasn't even sad when they had to operate on his wife because she had cancer, much less when we told him about my viejo . . . These sonofabitches are

gonna cut your hair, I'll see to that, if I have to bust their noses . . . There is
no devil, there isn't. The only devil is Don Rayos when he dresses up with
horns and with the cape to go to the shepherds' play . . . Goddamn fool!
Why don't you pay attention to what you're doing? You almost crashed with
that truck! Didn't you see it? Are you blind, or what? . . . Why did the
teacher cry when they came for him? Ever since he was put in her class she
always just kept looking at him. And she was so young, she wasn't like the
ones in Texas, little old ladies holding a paddle in their hands making sure
you didn't lose your place in the book. And if you did, pow! They'd just
bend you over . . . You think that was how they were burned? It's just hard
to believe. But so fast? It's that fire spreads fast and once your clothes catch
on fire, that's it. You remember that family that died in that fire around
Christmas time? They fell asleep, never to wake up again. And then the fire-
men crying as they removed the bodies, the grease from the children's little
burned up bodies dripping all over their boots . . . Free citizens, this is a day
of magnificent and profound importance. It was in the year eighteen-
hundred and seventy-two that Napoleon's troops suffered a defeat against
Mexican soldiers who fought so valiantly—that was how I would begin my
discourse. I always used the words "free citizens" when I was young, son,
but now ever since I had the attack I can't remember too well anymore what
I would say to the people. Then came the Revolution and in the end we lost.
Villa made out well but I had to come out here. No one here knows what I
went through. Sometimes I want to remember but, truth is, I'm not able to
anymore. All my thoughts become hazy. Now, tell me, what is it that you
most desire at this moment of your life? At this very moment . . . Yesterday
we collected fifty pounds of copper in all. Enrique found a magnet and that
makes it much easier to find the iron buried under so much junk that people
throw away. Sometimes we do well but usually it's a waste of time. But at
least enough to buy something to eat. And tell me, what's the price of tin
these days? Why don't you all come with us next time we go? . . . The cold
weather is setting in. I'll bet you that tomorrow morning the ground will be
all covered with frost. And notice how often the cranes fly by . . . There's
going to be a wedding Sunday. For sure they'll serve us cabrito in mole
sauce, with rice, and then the dance, and the groom, anxious for night to arrive . . . I tell you, comadre, we got so frightened last night when the lights
went out. We were there playing with the children when all of a sudden it
was pitch dark. And we didn't even have one candle. But that wasn't why
we got frightened. That knucklehead, Juan, was eating an orange and we
don't know how but he got a seed in his nose and we couldn't get it out in the
dark. And he was just crying and crying. And your compadre, lighting
match after match. I wonder what happened. Why all the lights of the town
went out . . . They found Doña Amada's son in a ditch and Don Tiburcio's

son inside the trailer. I think they're going to sue Don Jesús for transporting people in an closed van. They say that when they tried to stretch out his body, because they found him all curled up in a corner, when they tried to stretch him out to put him in the hearse, one of his legs fell off. . . Those people who sell those portraits don't come around here anymore. Don Mateo gave them a good scare . . . Mom nearly lost her mind. She always started crying whenever she talked with anyone about what happened to her downtown.

I would like to see all of the people together. And then, if I had great big arms, I could embrace them all. I wish I could talk to all of them again, but all of them together. But that, only in a dream. I like it right here because I can think about anything I please. Only by being alone can you bring every-body together. That's what I needed to do, hide, so that I could come to understand a lot of things. From now on, all I have to do is to come here, in the dark, and think about them. And I have so much to think about and I'm missing so many years. I think today what I wanted to do was recall this past year. And that's just one year. I'll have to come here to recall all of the other years.

He became aware of the present when he heard one of the children yelling and at the same time felt a blow to his leg. They were throwing rocks at him under the house.

"Mami, mami, there's a man under the house! Mami, mami, mami, hurry, come here, there's a man here, there's a man here!"

"Where? Where? Ah! . . . Let me get some boards and you run and get Doña Luz's dog."

And he saw countless faces and eyes looking at him. Then it grew darker under the house. The children kept throwing rocks at him and the dog kept barking while the woman was trying to poke him with some boards.

"Who could it be?"

He had to come out. Everyone was surprised that it was him. He didn't say anything to them, just walked away. And then he heard the woman say:

"That poor family. First the mother and now him. He must be losing his mind. He's losing track of the years."

Smiling, he walked down the chuckhole-ridden street leading to his house. He immediately felt happy because, as he thought over what the woman had said, he realized that in reality he hadn't lost anything. He had made a discovery. To discover and rediscover and piece things together. This to this, that to that, all with all. That was it. That was everything. He was thrilled. When he got home he went straight to the tree that was in the yard. He climbed it. He saw a palm tree on the horizon. He imagined someone perched on top, gazing across at him. He even raised one arm and waved it back and forth so that the other could see that he knew he was there.

Related Readings

from

Voices from the Fields:

S. Beth Atkin

Children of Migrant Farmworkers Tell Their Stories

S. Beth Atkin interviews children of migrant farmworkers who often struggle to receive the same education as their peers and sometimes give up school to work with their parents in the fields.

    Picking crops is a very hard way to earn money. The hours are long and the work physically demanding. While some growers treat their workers well, others pay poorly, withhold earned pay, or do not adhere to pesticide and sanitary regulations. By coming in contact with crops that have been sprayed with pesticides as well as with pesticides that drift from nearby fields and crop-dusting planes, fieldworkers risk developing acute skin and eye problems, chronic headaches, and cancer. Despite these problems, fieldworkers generally try to keep a positive attitude. They want to be hired again for the next season's harvest, and the pay is better than what they would get in Mexico.

    Nearly 20 percent of all pickers are under eighteen years of age. Agriculture is the only industry in the U.S. that legally employs children under sixteen. Because families need the money and parents have no one at home to babysit, young children work with their parents picking crops, arranging strawberries in a box, or tying up packages of vegetables. If children are under the legal age limits (ten for strawberries and potatoes and twelve for all other crops), they are not considered to be working but rather "helping out."

José Luis Ríos

Working in *La Fresa*

*Nine-year-old José Luis Ríos lives with his extended family
in a small house in Las Lomas, California. All of his
relatives work in the fields, including his brothers and
sisters. José Luis is often taken out of school to work
alongside his family. The owner of the land where the Ríos
family works has been charged by the investigators of the
Labor Department for violating some sixty provisions of
the federal Migrant and Seasonal Agricultural Worker
Protection Act.*

My NAME IS JOSÉ LUIS RÍOS, and I am in third grade. I have nine
brothers and sisters. We live with our parents and aunt and uncle and
cousins in Las Lomas. My grandparents live in Michoacan, Mexico. If they
were here right now, I'd ask them to come and visit because I don't know
them. My parents told me they used to work in the fields picking strawberries,
garbanzos, lentils, and corn. All my relatives that I can think of work in
the fields.

My parents work in *la fresa* [the strawberries] and *la mora* [the raspber-
ries], and my mom sometimes packs mushrooms. During the week, they
leave in the morning around six o'clock. I go and help them, mostly on
weekends. I help pick the strawberries and put them in boxes. Last year my
father took me to the fields a lot during the week, too, instead of bringing
me to school. I would find out I was going because he would say, "Let's go
pick strawberries now." I like going to the fields with my family because it is
pretty out there.

The longest day in the field was when we picked a lot of strawberries. I
felt bad and it was getting dark. We were out there so long. I said to my parents, "Let's go home," and finally they said, "We're going." It was hard to
work so long. My body gets tired, and when it is muddy, my feet get covered
with mud and it is hard to walk. Also, when it is muddy, my uncle has to
park the truck far away, and I get tired and cold when I have to walk back to
the truck.

My parents can't always find work. Usually there is work in the summer,
so then I help my father every day in the fields. I have to pull up the grass
around the strawberries, and I pick. I have to bend over. I bend over for a

long time. When I work in the fields with my father, I eat strawberries and he gives me *frijoles* [beans] sometimes when we stop to eat. We rest, and then we go back to work.

Sometimes when I'm there, my aunt and uncle that live with us are in the fields working. My cousins are there, too. I play with my cousin Andreas. He is seven. I like to play with him because he is a *buena gente* [good person]. We play tag in the fields. My brothers work in the fields but not usually my sisters. They go to school. Rogelio, my little brother who's two, comes to the fields, but he just plays. He doesn't make any trouble.

When I work in the fields, I don't get paid. I don't want them to pay me because it's not good. They pay my parents for what I pick. I like that my parents get paid because then they buy me toy cars and trucks or maybe a bicycle. My brothers get paid. Ignacio is eighteen, and he works during the week. He doesn't go to school now, but he used to go to high school. Manuel is the oldest, and he works in the fields in Salinas. I want to work in the fields like my brothers when I'm older, because I can eat a lot of strawberries and out there you can watch the birds.

But sometimes it is hard and I'm tired in school on Mondays because I worked on the weekend. I also get a lot of bad headaches, so sometimes I have to leave school early or go and rest in the nurse's office. When my father took me to the fields last year during the week, it was hard to study when I got home because I was tired. It is hard to work and go to school at the same time.

I like coming to school better than working in the fields. I go to school on the bus at seven-thirty. I like going to school to learn because then you know things. If you don't know anything and you go somewhere and somebody asks you to write something, you won't be able to. And when you're older you won't know anything. The people who haven't gone to school, they work in the fields.

I'm trying to learn English at school, but I like to speak Spanish because I'm understood better. I have more friends that speak Spanish than English. My parents tell me to study English, but I like studying the Native Americans best because they wrote, they did drawings, and they hunted buffalos. I like the Mayans. They made houses so the water couldn't get in when it rained. In school I like to write, too. I write about the birds because they are pretty and they fly. And I like to write about sheep and animals and also the Ninja Turtles.

When I get home from school, I have cookies. I eat most of my meals at school. My older brothers and sisters are there when I get home. They take care of me because my parents are working in the fields. My big sisters Carmela and Amelia help me with my homework and make cookies and coffee. Sometimes we take the strawberries from the fields home to eat. We make *fresa molida*—it's kind of a milkshake. Sometimes I take care of my little brothers and sister. I give them coffee and cookies. I have to watch out when I take care of them because cars come up our driveway and they could hit them. That's what happened to my little cousin. And sometimes we play right by the driveway. I play marbles with my brother Carlos and my cousin Jorge. I like to play hide-and-seek with my little sister Maria. My favorite place to hide is in the car.

When I'm bigger, I want to be a fieldworker and work in the strawberries because I like to work, and I want to do lots of other stuff. I would like to live for a time in Mexico, so I could know it. I would like to know my grandparents. I think it is different there, because there are more strawberries. If I had money when I'm older, I'd buy food, like milk, and other things. I don't want to have children when I grow up because I'll have to give them money. But if I did, I would want them to work in *la fresa*.

Victor Machuca

My *Familia*

Fifteen-year-old Victor Machuca came to the U. S. just over three years ago. Like many Mexican and Mexican-American children, he speaks of the vital role of his older siblings and of the strong bonds and values of his family.

I CAME TO CALIFORNIA from Cuernavaca, Morelos, in Mexico. My parents both come from very big families. I have twenty-three aunts and uncles and forty cousins. But my immediate family is small. There is my mother, father, and sisters, Eliuth, who is twenty, and María Cruz, who is eighteen. I'm fifteen. My father used to work in the fields in Mexico. He planted rice there. He works in the fields here, and when he can't find work, he does construction. My mother used to work here in *el tapeo de garlic* [the garlic harvest], but right now she is working in a carrot cannery. Since my parents didn't always have a lot of work, they didn't want to have a lot of children. They wouldn't be able to support them. I am close to my sisters and parents because they are my family and I have a right to be united with them.

My relatives are close because of their friendships. Most of my father's relatives lived in the same town in Mexico as we did. That is why we are closer to my father's family, like my grandparents. I respect them because they are older and because my parents have always shown me to have respect for them. Like my father does. He remembers them a lot now that he is in the United States, and he sends them money when he has extra. When I lived there and we went to visit them, they always received us well. We would fish at the river near their house. The memory I have of them is that whenever I fought with anyone, they told me that I had to fix the problem with the person I was fighting—that I shouldn't rely on them to solve it. I always remember that, and now if I have a problem, I work it out with that person and not my parents.

I only saw my grandparents on my mother's side twice a year. I remember that if anything ever happened to me, they helped me. When we did go to visit them, in Guerrero, we would ride on their donkey. Also I would help them in their orchard planting things. I liked to learn from them, like digging a bowl around the plants to keep the water in. Their orchard had banana, mango, papaya, and plum trees. When they came to visit us, they would always bring us things, like bread and their fruit and *cariño* [affection]. All my grandparents are important to me. But since we came to the United States, I don't see them much.

Now we only see my family in Mexico on long vacations. I'd like to visit them more, like my uncles and aunts. Every year we always celebrated Christmas with them in our house. There, in Cuernavaca, we owned our house, and there was room for all our family. Here, it is too expensive to own a house, and we don't exchange presents or prepare a special meal, like we did there. My favorite was the Christmas meal. It wasn't like an everyday meal. We had *posole*. It's corn cooked with *carne* [meat] and chili powder. My mother made tamales, sweet and chili, and we had a peach *atole*—it's a sweet milk dessert with rice. The whole family was there. All my father's relatives and some of my mother's. There were at least twenty of us. Here just my parents, sisters, and I celebrate, but simply, because sometimes we don't have enough money.

My family and I still do things together here; they are just different things from what we did in Mexico. When we first moved here, we all worked together. We worked in the *cebollitos* [green onion] fields. We worked as a family because it's faster. We helped each other. One person pulls the onion out of the ground, the other person shakes it, another cleans it, and then one of us ties them up together. I think doing things like working together is important. It makes our family stronger. Sometimes we stay home and I help my father work on our car. We try to eat dinner together, and when my parents aren't working too late, we go to church together. But my favorite thing to do with them is to go to the park to feed the ducks.

My parents don't think I should work in the fields when I get older. They tell me that I shouldn't lose a career like a lot of people in the fields. They've also told me that some people get sick because of the work they do in the fields. I think that they tell me these things for my well-being, so that I'll study and finish high school.

They say it would be good to go to college. My mother always says she wants me to be a doctor. My father says that if I don't become a doctor, I should become an architect. Most of the time, I think I would like to be a doctor to save people who are sick and to try to help people who need help. Sometimes though, I think I'd like to become a lawyer. I would help people get their papers and then people, like my family and others I know, could cross *la frontera* [the border] from Mexico, legally, instead of risking their lives crossing mountains.

My parents would like me to go to college, but they don't tell me that

I have to. One reason I want to go to college is that I admire Eliuth and María Cruz because they are both in college here and they speak English well. I would like to be at their level of English, but I didn't learn how to conjugate the verbs in junior high. I think I'd prefer to go to college in Mexico, because of the language and it's faster there. It's also very expensive here. My sisters tell me not to quit and that I should keep trying with my English, and that if I go to college here, maybe I can get migrant scholarships like they have.

My sisters have always helped me and given me advice. When I was little, they took care of me when my parents were working. If something happened to me, like if I fell down, they cured me. I have good memories of them taking care of me. If anything ever happened to my parents, I would work and try to take care of my sisters. But I know they would encourage me not to fall behind in school just to help them. I know they would try to help me, too. When we are older, if my sisters have children and visit me, I would treat them well. I would give them food and help them if they needed to go somewhere. I would always help them and my parents.

For example, when my parents get older, if they can't work, I'll help them. They always help me and have given me food since I was little, so I would like to do the same for them. Sometimes now I would like to be able to give them money. If I was making, let's say, fifty dollars a week, I would give all the money to them and they would give me back what I needed.

I think my friends feel like I do about their families. Their parents are important to them, and they listen to their advice. I have some friends that do not respect their family. Their parents tell them that they don't like their kids to smoke, but they smoke anyway. I listen to my parents, because they always give me good advice. If I ever have children, I would want them to listen to my parents also. I would want them to respect their grandparents.

When I get older, I want to live close to my family, all of them. There isn't anything more important than my family. I feel an obligation to be with them, not because they tell me to but because I feel this. It is my own will to be with them. They help me in everything, and they are the only family I have.

Andrea Martínez

Fitting In

*Eighteen-year-old Andrea Martínez, a Zapotec Indian
from Oaxaca, in southern Mexico, spoke neither Spanish
nor English when she moved to the U. S. several years
ago. She was not only isolated from her family and the
Zapotec language but also ostracized by schoolmates
because she did not speak Spanish.*

I AM FROM EL MIRADOR, a village near the town of Ojitlan, by the city
of Tuxtepect, in that state of Oaxaca, Mexico. I am a Zapotec *indio* [Indian].
Zapotec is a kind of *indígena* [native] group from Mexico. The dialect we
speak is Zapoteca. My grandparents are Zapotec and were born on the *ranchita* [small ranch] I lived on, and they worked off the land, planting seeds,
harvesting the crops, and selling them if there was extra. My mother grew
up there also. My real father was from around there, too. But I never really
knew him. My grandmother raised me so my mother could work in Mexico
City.

I started working on the *ranchita* when I was eight, harvesting chilies,
corn, and coffee. Lots of children did the same. There were about fifty families living in our community then. Everyone had their own land, which had
been divided up by a committee. The committee was also supposed to collect
money for the school. But most of the parents said the school didn't work.
They preferred their children to work in the fields instead of studying. Many
people where I grew up thought that if you are a girl, you are just supposed
to get married. That is what my grandmother thought, so I worked, and my
brothers went to school. My grandmother told me, "Since you are a girl, you
are not supposed to study." She thought that girls were lowly. So as you can
see, I have known discrimination since I was small. Another way I've
known it is growing up in Mexico and being Zapotec. Even though we come
from the same blood, the Mexicans would discriminate against us because
we were Indian. They would say, "Indio, get to work." That is because we
are poor, and we had to work hard.

I moved to the Salinas Valley four years ago with my mother and my brother Francisco. My brother Sergio stayed in Mexico. I have a little sister, also, named Marilyn. She was born here just a year ago. My stepfather, who is her father, came with us from Mexico, too, but I didn't know him because my mother met him after she left the *ranchita*. My mother first worked here mostly in the grapes. But now I don't get to see her much because she works a lot in Yuma, Arizona, in *la lechuga* [the lettuce]. It's difficult, and every day I miss her. When we first moved I felt alone here. My mother would leave to work, and it was really hard because my stepfather only speaks Spanish. I couldn't talk to him because I only spoke Zapoteca. Where I grew up, the only time I ever heard Spanish was when an outsider came and someone would talk in Spanish out of need. If someone spoke to us in Spanish, we were afraid because we didn't understand what they were saying. We were also embarrassed that we couldn't talk back to them.

Everything here was different from where I grew up: the food, the people, the clothes. But the hardest part for me when I moved was the language. I couldn't speak Spanish, and I didn't know English. Also no one in my community in Mexico knew how to write or even how to pick up a pencil. My mother told me that things would be better soon because here at least I could get an education.

There is nothing similar about Zapoteca and Spanish, and it took me a year just to learn Spanish. My stepfather talked to one of my teachers and explained that I didn't know Spanish. In my Spanish class the teacher had her aide help me a lot. Little by little, she taught me how to make sentences. But learning English was harder. I stayed in the same level for two years. The English class had all Mexicans, and I had a classmate who tried to help me a lot. She is still my friend. But she only spoke Spanish, and so I didn't really understand. In other subjects, I was put in classes that were too advanced for me because I didn't know the language. Like in social studies: the teacher told me I should raise my hand more in class. She knew that I had the answers, like the capitals of countries in Central America. But I didn't know how to say the answers. So I stayed after school, and she helped me. Then I advanced in the class and got an A. I was lucky because a lot of teachers helped me.

My mother encouraged me a lot when she was home. I didn't know how to defend myself, and she helped me. She told me to try to speak in Spanish and not to quit even though the students were making fun of me. They pulled my hair and they called me a *mensa* [fool]. They insulted me. The *pochas* especially—their parents are from Mexico but they were born here and speak mostly English. They think they are great and that once they know a little English they are *gabachas* [*gringos*, non-Mexicans]. They called me "*indio*" to insult me because that is what they call people who just came from Mexico. But what they didn't know is that I am a true Indian.

For me, the *pochas* are worse than the *gabachas*. The time I went on a field trip, for the FBLA [Future Business Leaders of America], everybody treated me really well. They weren't Mexican, and when I told them I couldn't speak English well, they said, "Andrea, you can speak very well." I've also taken an English literature class, and not one American made fun of me. But I know that some Mexicans here have problems and are treated badly. In King City, which is right nearby, some high school students want a school newspaper in Spanish, but the school won't let them have it. So maybe it is easier here for Americans than Mexicans. But I'm not sure because I usually don't see what problems Americans confront, only the ones Mexicans have. What I do think is Americans educate their children better.

The hardest problem for Mexicans is that they need to know English to live here. They have a hard time knowing only Spanish. But most of them have had an education in Mexico. There are not a lot of students who have had to face what I did. It's not that I'm the only one, but when I moved to the United States, I hadn't gone to school, and I couldn't communicate at all.

Now things are better because I have friends. Before if some girls would walk by me and say, "Hi. How are you?" I was too embarrassed to talk to them in Spanish. I was afraid. Now I'm not. Also, since I've come here I have had the opportunity for an education and I'm learning a lot. One of the best experiences I've had is going to the Yo Puedo [I Can] program. It is a special summer program at a college campus in Santa Cruz that helps children of migrant workers. It motivates them to go forward and improve their lives. A lot of people helped me with the Yo Puedo application, and I got in. Just getting accepted gave me more confidence because I never thought I would. Nobody made fun of me there, and being at a university was really nice. The program helped me in many ways. I learned computers there, and now I want to become a computer engineer when I go to college. It also made me more comfortable to be in the United States.

Now that I have finished the program, I'm still learning through Advanced Leadership Training sessions. Once a month, all the Yo Puedo students teach little migrant children to try hard and be motivated in school. I tell them to never quit school. We have workshops and do skits on subjects like self-esteem, language barriers, and discrimination. One day I will stand up and speak at a workshop on discrimination. Because the kids in the program should see that it's not just the Americans that discriminate against us but also Mexicans who are born here, the *pochas*, who discriminate against other Mexicans, too. I don't want to offend them but I would tell them, "You will know what it is like when you go to university and feel discrimination, because Americans will see you as Mexican." Then maybe they will notice that discrimination is everywhere.

Since I have been here for a while, I now know what it feels like to be Mexican. I speak Spanish and have friends that are Mexican. But I still think my Zapotec heritage is important. I don't speak my dialect much, because my mother isn't around. But I try to think about it by myself. It is important not to lose it, because it is in my blood. If I had to choose between being Mexican and Zapotec, I'd choose both. Because I can't discriminate against Zapotecas, my people.

Langston
Hughes

Christmas

*In both Tomás Rivera's novel and Langston Hughes's short
story, the hardships of poverty are felt during the
Christmas season as parents struggle to find a way to buy
their children gifts.*

Po' LITTLE THING," said Hager. "Po' little thing. An' here we ain't got
no money."

The night before, on Saturday, Hager had bought a sack of flour, a chunk
of salt pork, and some groceries. Old Dr. McDillors had called in the afternoon, and she had paid him, too.

"I reckon it would take mo'n thirty dollars to send fo' Harriett, an' Lawd
knows we ain't got three dollars in de house."

Annjee lay limply back on her pillows staring out of the window at the
falling snow. She had been crying.

"But never mind," her mother went on, "I's gwine see Mr. John Frank
tomorrow an' see can't I borry a little mo' money on this mortgage we's got
with him."

So on Monday morning the old lady left her washing and went uptown
to the office of the money-lender, but the clerk there said Mr. Frank had
gone to Chicago and would not be back for two weeks. There was nothing
the clerk could do about it, since he himself could not lend money.

That afternoon Annjee sat up in bed and wrote a long letter to Harriett,
telling her of their troubles, and before she sealed it, Sandy saw his mother
slip into the envelope the three one-dollar bills that she had been guarding
under her pillow.

"There goes your Santa Claus," she said to her son, "but maybe Harriett's
hungry. And you don't want Aunt Harrie to be hungry, do you?"

"No'm," Sandy said.

The grey days passed and Annjee was able to get up and sit beside the kitchen-stove while her mother ironed. Every afternoon Sandy went downtown to look at the shop windows, gay with Christmas things. And he would stand and stare at the Golden Flyer sleds in Edmondson's hardware-shop. He could feel himself coasting down a long hill on one of those light, swift, red and yellow coasters, the envy of all the other boys, white and colored, who looked on.

When he went home, he described the sled minutely[1] to Annjee and Aunt Hager and wondered aloud if that might be what he would get for Christmas. But Hager would say: "Santa Claus are just like other folks. He don't work for nothin'!" And his mother would add weakly from her chair: "This is gonna be a slim Christmas, honey, but mama'll see what she can do." She knew his heart was set on a sled, and he could tell that she knew; so maybe he would get it.

One day Annjee gathered her strength together, put a woollen dress over her kimono,[2] wrapped a heavy cloak about herself, and went out into the back yard. Sandy, from the window, watched her picking her way slowly across the frozen ground towards the outhouse. At the trash-pile near the alley fence she stopped and, stooping down, began to pull short pieces of boards and wood from the little pile of lumber that had been left there since last summer by the carpenters who had built the porch. Several times in her labor she rose and leaned weakly against the back fence for support, and once Sandy ran out to see if he could help her, but she told him irritably to get back in the house out of the weather or she would put him to bed without any supper. Then, after placing the boards that she had succeeded in unearthing in a pile by the path, she came wearily back to the kitchen, trembling with cold.

"I'm mighty weak yet," she said to Hager, "but I'm sure much better than I was. I don't want to have the grippe[3] no more. . . . Sandy, look in the mailbox and see has the mail-man come by yet."

As the little boy returned empty-handed, he heard his mother talking about old man Logan, who used to be a carpenter.

"Maybe he can make it," she was saying, but stopped when she heard Sandy behind her. "I guess I'll lay back down now."

Aunt Hager wrung out the last piece of clothes that she had been rinsing. "Yes, chile," she said, "you go on and lay down. I's gwine make you some tea after while." And the old woman went outdoors to take from the line the frozen garments blowing in the sharp north wind.

---

1. minutely in detail
2. kimono loose robe or dress
3. grippe flu

After supper that night Aunt Hager said casually: "Well, I reckon I'll run down an' see Brother Logan a minute whilst I got nothin' else to do. Sandy, don't you let de fire go out, and take care o' yo' mama."

"Yes'm," said the little boy, drawing pictures on the oilcloth-covered table with a pin. His grandmother went out the back door and he looked through the frosty window to see which way she was going. The old woman picked up the boards that his mother had piled near the alley fence, and with them in her arms she disappeared down the alley in the dark.

After a little, Aunt Hager returned puffing and blowing.

"Can he do it?" Annjee demanded anxiously from the bedroom when she heard her mother enter.

"Yes, chile," Hager answered. "Lawd, it sho is cold out yonder! Whee! Lemme git here to this stove!"

That night it began to snow again. The great heavy flakes fell with languid[4] gentility over the town and silently the whiteness covered everything. The next morning the snow froze to a hard sparkling crust on roofs and ground, and in the late afternoon when Sandy went to return the Reinharts' clothes, you could walk on top of the snow without sinking.

At the back door of the Reinharts' house a warm smell of plum-pudding and mince pies drifted out as he waited for the cook to bring the money. When she returned with seventy-five cents, she had a nickel for Sandy, too. As he slid along the street, he saw in many windows gay holly wreaths with red berries and big bows of ribbon tied to them. Sandy wished he could buy a holly wreath for their house. It might make his mother's room look cheerful. At home it didn't seem like Christmas with the kitchen full of drying clothes, and no Christmas-tree.

Sandy wondered if, after all, Santa Claus might, by some good fortune, bring him that Golden Flyer sled on Christmas morning. How fine this hard snow would be to coast on, down the long hill past the Hickory Woods! How light and swift he would fly with his new sled! Certainly he had been a good boy, carrying Aunt Hager's clothes for her, waiting on his mother when she was in bed, emptying the slops and cutting wood every day. And at night when he said his prayers:

> Now I lay me down to sleep.
> Pray the Lord my soul to keep.
> If I should die before I wake,
> Pray the Lord my soul to take. . . .

---

4. languid lifeless

he had added with great earnestness: "And let Santa bring me a Golden Flyer sled, please, Lord. Amen."

But Sandy knew very well that there wasn't really any Santa Claus! He knew in his heart that Hager and his mother were Santa Claus—and that they didn't have any money. They were poor people. He was wearing his mama's shoes, as Jimmy Lane had once done. And his father and Harriett, who used to make the house gay, laughing and singing, were far away somewhere. . . . There wasn't any Santa Claus.

"I don't care," he said, tramping over the snow in the twilight on his way from the Reinharts'.

Christmas Eve. Candles and poinsettia flowers. Wreaths of evergreen. Baby trees hung with long strands of tinsel and fragile ornaments of colored glass. Sandy passed the windows of many white folks' houses where the curtains were up and warm floods of electric light made bright the cozy rooms. In Negro shacks, too, there was the dim warmth of oil-lamps and Christmas candles glowing. But at home there wasn't even a holly wreath. And the snow was whiter and harder than ever on the ground.

Tonight, though, there were no clothes drying in the kitchen when he went in. The ironing-board had been put away behind the door, and the whole place was made tidy and clean. The fire blazed and crackled in the little range; but nothing else said Christmas—no laughter, no tinsel, no tree.

Annjee had been about all day, still weak, but this afternoon she had made a trip to the store for a quarter's worth of mixed candies and nuts and a single orange, which she had hidden away until morning. Hager had baked a little cake, but there was no frosting on it such as there had been in other years, and there were no strange tissue-wrapped packages stuck away in the corners of trunks and drawers days ahead of time.

Although the little kitchen was warm enough, the two bedrooms were chilly, and the front room was freezing-cold because they kept the door there closed all the time. It was hard to afford a fire in one stove, let alone two, Aunt Hager kept saying, with nobody working but herself.

"I's thinking about Harriett," she remarked after their Christmas Eve supper as she rocked before the fire, "and how I's always tried to raise her right."

"And I'm thinking about—well, there ain't no use mentionin' him," Annjee said.

A sleigh slid by with jingling bells and shouts of laughter from the occupants, and a band of young people passed on their way to church, singing carols. After a while another sleigh came along with a jolly sound.

"Santa Claus!" said Annjee, smiling at her serious little son. "You better hurry and go to bed, because he'll be coming soon. And be sure to hang up your stocking."

But Sandy was afraid that she was fooling, and, as he pulled off his clothes, he left his stockings on the floor, stuck into the women's shoes he had been wearing. Then, leaving the bedroom door half open so that the heat and a little light from the kitchen would come in, he climbed into his mother's bed. But he wasn't going to close his eyes yet. Sandy had discovered long ago that you could hear and see many things by not going to sleep when the family expected you to; therefore he remained awake tonight.

His mother was talking to Aunt Hager now: "I don't think he'll charge us anything, do you, ma?" And the old woman answered: "No, chile, Brother Logan's been tryin' to be ma beau for twenty years, an' he ain't gonna charge us nothin'."

Annjee came into the half-dark bedroom and looked at Sandy, lying still on the side of the bed towards the window. Then she took down her heavy coat from the wall and, sitting on the edge of a chair, began to pull on her rubbers. In a few moments he heard the front door close softly. His mother had gone out.

Where could she be going, he wondered, this time of night? He heard her footsteps crunching the hard snow and, rolling over close to the window, he pulled aside the shade a little and looked out. In the moonlight he saw Annjee moving slowly down the street past Sister Johnson's house, walking carefully over the snow like a very weak woman.

"Mama's still sick," the child thought, with his nose pressed against the cold window-pane. "I wish I could a bought her a present today."

Soon an occasional snore from the kitchen told Sandy that Hager dozed peacefully in her rocker beside the stove. He sat up in bed, wrapped a quilt about his shoulders, and remained looking out the window, with the shade hanging behind his back.

The white snow sparkled in the moonlight, and the trees made striking black shadows across the yard. Next door at the Johnson's all was dark and quiet, but across the street, where white folks lived, the lights were burning brightly and a big Christmas-tree with all its candles aglow stood in the large bay window while a woman loaded it with toys. Sandy knew that four children lived there, three boys and a girl, whom he had often watched playing on the lawn. Sometimes he wished he had a brother or sister to play with him, too, because it was very quiet in a house with only grown-ups about. And right now it was dismal and lonely to be by himself looking out the window of a cold bedroom on Christmas Eve.

Then a woman's cloaked figure came slowly back past Sister Johnson's house in the moonlight, and Sandy saw that it was his mother returning, her head down and her shadow moving blackly on the snow. You could hear the dry grate of her heels on the frozen whiteness as she walked, leaning forward, dragging something heavy behind her. Sandy prepared to lie down quickly in bed again, but he kept his eyes against the window-pane to see what Annjee was pulling, and, as she came closer to the house, he could distinguish quite clearly behind her a solid, home-made sled bumping rudely over the snow.

Before Annjee's feet touched the porch, he was lying still as though he had been asleep a long time.

The morning sunlight was tumbling brightly into the windows when Sandy opened his eyes and blinked at the white world outside.

"Aren't you ever going to get up?" asked Annjee, smiling timidly above him. "It's Christmas morning, honey. Come see what Santa Claus brought you. Get up quick."

But he didn't want to get up. He knew what Santa Claus had brought him and he wanted to stay in bed with his face to the wall. It wasn't a Golden Flyer sled—and now he couldn't even hope for one any longer. He wanted to pull the covers over his head and cry, but, "Boy! You ain't up yet?" called Aunt Hager cheerily from the kitchen. "De little Lawd Jesus is in His manger fillin' all de world with light. An' old Santa done been here an' gone! Get out from there, chile, an' see!"

"I'm coming, grandma," said Sandy slowly, wiping his tear-filled eyes and rolling out of bed as he forced his mouth to smile wide and steady at the few little presents he saw on the floor—for the child knew he was expected to smile.

"O! A sled!" he cried in a voice of mock surprise that wasn't his own at all; for there it stood, heavy and awkward, against the wall and beside it on the floor lay two picture-books from the ten-cent store and a pair of white cotton gloves. Above the sled his stocking, tacked to the wall, was partly filled with candy, and the single orange peeped out from the top.

But the sled! Home-made by some rough carpenter, with strips of rusty tin nailed along the wooden runners, and a piece of clothes-line to pull it with!

"It's fine," Sandy lied, as he tried to lift it and place it on the floor as you would in coasting; but it was very heavy, and too wide for a boy to run with in his hands. You could never get a swift start. And a board was warped in the middle.

"It's a nice sled, grandma," he lied. "I like it, mama."

"Mr. Logan made it for you," his mother answered proudly, happy that he was pleased. "I knew you wanted a sled all the time."

"It's a nice sled," Sandy repeated, grinning steadily as he held the heavy object in his hands. "It's an awful nice sled."

"Well, make haste and look at de gloves, and de candy, and them pretty books, too," called Hager from the kitchen, where she was frying strips of salt pork. "My, you sho is a slow chile on Christmas mawin'! Come 'ere and lemme kiss you." She came to the bedroom and picked him up in her arms. "Christmas gift to Hager's baby chile! Come on, Annjee, bring his clothes out here behind de stove an' bring his books, too. . . . This here's Little Red Riding Hood and the Wolf, and this here's Hansee and Gretsle on de cover—but I reckon you can read 'em better'n I can. . . . Daughter, set de table. Breakfast's 'bout ready now. Look in de oven an' see 'bout that corn-bread. Lawd, this here Sandy's just like a baby lettin' ole Hager hold him and dress him. . . . Put yo' foot in that stocking, boy!" And Sandy began to feel happier, sitting on his grandmother's lap behind the stove.

Before noon Buster had come and gone, showing off his new shoes and telling his friend about the train he had gotten that ran on a real track when you wound it up. After dinner Willie-Mae appeared bringing a naked rag doll and a set of china dishes in a blue box. And Sister Johnson sent them a mince pie as a Christmas gift.

Almost all Aunt Hager's callers knocked at the back door, but in the late afternoon the front bell rang and Annjee sent Sandy through the cold par-lor to answer it. There on the porch stood his Aunt Tempy, with several gaily wrapped packages in her arms. She was almost a stranger to Sandy, yet she kissed him peremptorily[5] on the forehead as he stood in the doorway. Then she came through the house into the kitchen, with much the air of a mistress of the manor descending to the servants' quarters.

"Lands sakes alive!" said Hager, rising to kiss her.

Tempy hugged Annjee, too, before she sat down, stiffly, as though the house she was in had never been her home. To little Willie-Mae she said nothing.

"I'm sorry I couldn't invite you for Christmas dinner today, but you know how Mr. Siles is," Tempy began to explain to her mother and sister. "My husband is home so infrequently, and he doesn't like a house full of company, but of course Dr. and Mrs. Glenn Mitchell will be in later in the evening. They drop around any time. . . . But I had to run down and bring you a few presents. . . . You haven't seen my new piano yet, have you, mother? I must come and take you home with me some nice afternoon." She smiled appropriately, but her voice was hard.

"How is you an' yo' new church makin' it?" asked Hager, slightly embar-rassed in the presence of her finely dressed society daughter.

"Wonderful!" Tempy replied. "Wonderful! Father Hill is so dignified, and the services are absolutely refined! . . . so you know, mother, they suit me."

---

5. **peremptorily** with disregard of an objection

"I's glad you likes it," said Hager.

There was an awkward silence; then Tempy distributed her gifts, kissed them all as though it were her Christian duty, and went her way, saying that she had calls to make at Lawyer and Mrs. Moore's, and Professor Booth's, and Madam Temple's before she returned home. When she had gone, everybody felt relieved—as though a white person had left the house. Willie-Mae began to play again, and Hager pushed her feet out of her shoes once more, while Annjee went into the bedroom and lay down.

Sandy sat on the floor and untied his present, wrapped in several thicknesses of pink tissue paper, and found, in a bright Christmas box, a big illustrated volume of Andersen's Fairy Tales decorated in letters of gold. With its heavy pages and fine pictures, it made the ten-cent-store books that Hager had bought him appear cheap and thin. It made his mother's sled look cheap, too, and shamed all the other gifts the ones he loved had given him.

"I don't want it," he said suddenly, as loud as he could. "I don't want Tempy's old book!" And from where he was sitting, he threw it with all his might underneath the stove.

Hager gasped in astonishment. "Pick that up, sir," she cried, amazed. "Yo' Aunt Tempy done bought you a fine purty book an' here you throwin' it un'neath de stove in de ashes! Lawd have mercy! Pick it up, I say, this minute!"

"I won't!" cried Sandy stubbornly. "I won't! I like my sled what you-all gave me, but I don't want no old book from Tempy! I won't pick it up!"

Then the astonished Hager grabbed him by the scruff of the neck and jerked him to his feet.

"Do I have to whip you yet this holy day? . . . Pick up that book, sir!"

"No!" he yelled.

She gave him a startled rap on the head with the back of her hand. "Talkin' sassy to yo' old grandma an' tellin' her no!"

"What is it?" Annjee called from the bedroom, as Sandy began to wail.

"Nothin'," Hager replied, " 'ceptin' this chile's done got beside hisself an' I has to hit him—that's all!"

But Sandy was not hurt by his grandmother's easy rap. He was used to being struck on the back of the head for misdemeanors, and this time he welcomed the blow because it gave him, at last, what he had been looking for all day—a sufficient excuse to cry. Now his pent-up tears flowed without ceasing while Willie-Mae sat in a corner clutching her rag doll to her breast, and Tempy's expensive gift lay in the ashes beneath the stove.

| Verena Dobnik and Ted Anthony | # Children for Hire |

Associated Press reporters Verena Dobnik and Ted Anthony examine the lives of children who work in the fields and factories of America.

They are children, yes. But is this childhood?

She sweats into the soil of a vast Ohio field. A baseball cap keeps the sun and her unruly dark hair from her almond eyes. Adult rubber gloves engulf the small hands that snap cucumbers from their vines. Her name is Alejandra Renteria. She is 6.

Six hundred miles away, a girl who dreams of being a fashion designer fingers a cheap jacket in a Manhattan sweatshop, where rats scurry across dirty floors. Amid noisy machines and the hubbub of women stitching, Li-qing Ni laments: "I like New York, but not this place. It smells." She is 15. . . .

Some are very young. Others are approaching adulthood. From America's fields they harvest onions, peppers, mushrooms, beans, berries, pecans. In garment factories, they iron pants, hang shirts, trim clothing. In meat-packing and egg-producing plants, in sawmills and furniture factories they toil.

Among them are an estimated 61,000 child field workers, ages 14 to 17, who live apart from their parents, according to an unreleased U.S. Labor Department survey. In thousands of cases, their parents aren't even in the country. In all, about 123,000 children in that age group work in America's fields, the survey said. Younger children in the fields are an all-but hidden, untracked work force.

At least 13,100 more children worked illegally last year in garment industry sweatshops—factories that repeatedly violate federal wages and hours laws—a study commissioned by The Associated Press found.

Children often underpaid, underprotected

Federal law bars children under 16 from working while school is in session. Outside school hours, anyone 14 or 15 may work in farm jobs that the U.S. Labor Department deems safe. Younger children, those 12 or 13, can work only on farms and at a few other specified jobs.

Many of the children working in America are underpaid, often unaccompanied and largely unprotected—a shadow generation made prematurely adult, moving from coast to coast, border to border.

"Farmers used to own slaves. Now they rent them," says Diane Mull, executive director of the nonprofit Association of Farm Worker Opportunity Programs in Arlington, Va. "The agrarian[1] myth is dead."

Few myths ever surrounded sweatshops. In New York City, the hub of the American garment trade, a group of reformers known as Progressives led the anti-child labor movement of the early 1900s, leading to a 1938 law to protect children.

In 1997, that progress has not reached the Chinatown factory where Li-qing, the girl who dreams of being a designer, prepares clothing for her mother to stitch. They immigrated from China's poor Fujian province months ago, and this third-floor assembly line of women and sewing machines is now their America.

Li-qing doesn't know where her father is, and one day recently a state labor investigator who visited the factory told her she couldn't help her mother earn a living. "Don't come back again," he said. "It's illegal."

Kids work because parents are poor

Why do they live these lives?

Some kids want spending money to buy into the consumer culture they see as necessary to being American. But many, especially migrant children, work because their parents don't earn enough.

"If adults were paid a living wage, we wouldn't have child labor," says Ann Millard, a Michigan State University anthropologist who studies migrant labor. Three out of four migrant families say they earn $5,000 or less yearly according to a national database of 54,000 families compiled by Mull's group.

Eluding rarely enforced laws, these workers bypass the modern Western concept of children as virtually a separate society—one to be protected, educated and prepped for adulthood rather than forced into it.

Near Ohio cucumber fields, the five members of the Mares family live in a one-room shack with no running water. The children fantasize about what many American kids take for granted,—"our own house, with my own

---

1. **agrarian** agricultural

room," says Fabiola Mares, 12.

For them, even normal childhood friendships aren't easy. When Laura Mares, 10, received a rare invitation to a classmate's birthday party, "she couldn't go," says her mother, Elvira. "We just didn't have the money to buy a gift."

Children toil but dream of better life

In Bowling Green, Ohio, American flags grace nearly every block of Main Street. Those who work the surrounding farmland rarely venture into this college town. They are moving specks in the lush landscape, forgotten among red barns, white steeples and stretches of corn, tomatoes and wheat.

This is where Alejandra, the 6-year-old with the oversized rubber gloves, spent the most recent summer of her childhood. She and her family rode 1,000 miles from Florida in a faded green Oldsmobile to pick cucumbers.

Her father, Marcelo Renteria, a 30-year-old with a third-grade education, voices a hope that has driven immigrant America for generations. "I want the kids to study," he says, "so they don't end up like me."

Alejandra wants to work with computers, and her 9-year-old sister wants to be a teacher. But for now they must help the family survive.

Some, like Yvonne Li, do get out.

When she was 6, she went from school to a New York City garment factory to help her grandmother button, sew and trim clothing with scissors. "It was hot and humid," she recalls. "The bathroom was always yucky."

That stopped when her mother found out. Now a happy 9-year-old, Yvonne can no longer remember the name of the factory. She's far more concerned with professional basketball standings and her favorite subject in school—math. Asked what she wants to be, she raises both fists and shouts, "The best at whatever I do!"

The working kids she leaves behind have their hopes, too, reaching beyond produce fields and garment shops for education, careers, success—and a need to just be kids.

Alex Ledezma, 11, harvests sorghum,[2] cotton and onions near Lubbock, Texas. Though he misses weeks of school each year to follow the crops, he has reached sixth grade. He makes $2.25 an hour hoeing. He wants to become a policeman.

Beside the sorghum plants that tower above his head sits a van that carries his family and the hoes to the field. On its rear window is a sticker.

It says, "I believe in America."

---

2. **sorghum** a type of grain

First Confession

Frank O'Connor

Young boys in Tomás Rivera's novel and Frank O'Conner's short story find that the anticipation of a first confession can be a very traumatic experience.

ALL THE TROUBLE BEGAN when my grandfather died and my grandmother—my father's mother—came to live with us. Relations in the one house are a strain at the best of times, but, to make matters worse, my grandmother was a real old countrywoman and quite unsuited to the life in town. She had a fat, wrinkled old face, and, to Mother's great indignation, went round the house in bare feet—the boots had her crippled, she said. For dinner she had a jug of porter[1] and a pot of potatoes with—sometimes—a bit of salt fish, and she poured out the potatoes on the table and ate them slowly, with great relish, using her fingers by way of a fork.

Now, girls are supposed to be fastidious,[2] but I was the one who suffered most from this. Nora, my sister, just sucked up to the old woman for the penny she got every Friday out of the old-age pension, a thing I could not do. I was too honest, that was my trouble; and when I was playing with Bill Connell, the sergeant-major's son, and saw my grandmother steering up the path with the jug of porter sticking out from beneath her shawl I was mortified. I made excuses not to let him come into the house, because I could never be sure what she would be up to when we went in.

When Mother was at work and my grandmother made the dinner I wouldn't touch it. Nora once tried to make me, but I hid under the table from her and took the bread-knife with me for protection. Nora let on to be very indignant (she wasn't, of course, but she knew Mother saw through her, so she sided with Gran) and came after me. I lashed out at her with the bread-knife, and after that she left me alone. I stayed there till Mother came in from work and made my dinner, but when Father came in later Nora said

---

1. **porter** dark beer
2. **fastidious** having high standards, particularly with respect to manners

in a shocked voice: "Oh, Dadda, do you know what Jackie did at dinner-time?" Then, of course, it all came out; Father gave me a flaking; Mother interfered, and for days after that he didn't speak to me and Mother barely spoke to Nora. And all because of that old woman! God knows, I was heart-scalded.

Then, to crown my misfortunes, I had to make my first confession and communion. It was an old woman called Ryan who prepared us for these. She was about the one age with Gran; she was well-to-do, lived in a big house on Montenotte, wore a black cloak and bonnet, and came every day to school at three o'clock when we should have been going home, and talked to us of hell. She may have mentioned the other place as well, but that could only have been by accident, for hell had the first place in her heart.

She lit a candle, took out a new half-crown, and offered it to the first boy who would hold one finger—only one finger!—in the flame for five minutes by the school clock. Being always very ambitious I was tempted to volunteer, but I thought it might look greedy. Then she asked were we afraid of holding one finger—only one finger!—in a little candle flame for five minutes and not afraid of burning all over in roasting hot furnaces for all eternity. "All eternity! Just think of that! A whole lifetime goes by and it's nothing, not even a drop in the ocean of your sufferings." The woman was really interesting about hell, but my attention was all fixed on the half-crown. At the end of the lesson she put it back in her purse. It was a great disap-pointment; a religious woman like that, you wouldn't think she'd bother about a thing like a half-crown.

Another day she said she knew a priest who woke one night to find a fellow he didn't recognize leaning over the end of his bed. The priest was a bit frightened—naturally enough—but he asked the fellow what he wanted, and the fellow said in a deep, husky voice that he wanted to go to confession. The priest said it was an awkward time and wouldn't it do in the morning, but the fellow said that last time he went to confession, there was one sin he kept back, being ashamed to mention it, and now it was always on his mind. Then the priest knew it was a bad case, because the fellow was after making a bad confession and committing a mortal sin. He got up to dress, and just then the cock crew in the yard outside, and—lo and behold!—when the priest looked round there was no sign of the fellow, only a smell of burning timber, and when the priest looked at his bed didn't he see the print of two hands burned in it? That was because the fellow had made a bad confession. This story made a shocking impression on me.

But the worst of all was when she showed us how to examine our con-science. Did we take the name of the Lord, our God, in vain? Did we honour our father and our mother? (I asked her did this include grandmothers and she said it did.) Did we love our neighbours as ourselves? Did we covet[3] our neighbour's goods? (I thought of the way I felt about the penny that Nora got every Friday.) I decided that, between one thing and another, I must have broken the whole ten commandments, all on account of that old woman, and so far as I could see, so long as she remained in the house I had no hope of ever doing anything else.

I was scared to death of confession. The day the whole class went I let on to have a toothache, hoping my absence wouldn't be noticed; but at three o'clock, just as I was feeling safe, along comes a chap with a message from Mrs. Ryan that I was to go to confession myself on Saturday and be at the chapel for communion with the rest. To make it worse, Mother couldn't come with me and sent Nora instead.

Now, that girl had ways of tormenting me that Mother never knew of. She held my hand as we went down the hill, smiling sadly and saying how sorry she was for me, as if she were bringing me to the hospital for an operation.

"Oh, God help us!" she moaned. "Isn't it a terrible pity you weren't a good boy? Oh, Jackie, my heart bleeds for you! How will you ever think of all your sins? Don't forget you have to tell him about the time you kicked Gran on the shin."

"Lemme go!" I said, trying to drag myself free of her. "I don't want to go to confession at all."

"But sure, you'll have to go to confession, Jackie," she replied in the same regretful tone. "Sure, if you didn't, the parish priest would be up to the house, looking for you. 'Tisn't, God knows, that I'm not sorry for you. Do you remember the time you tried to kill me with the bread-knife under the table? And the language you used to me? I don't know what he'll do with you at all, Jackie. He might have to send you up to the bishop."

I remember thinking bitterly that she didn't know the half of what I had to tell—if I told it. I knew I couldn't tell it, and understood perfectly why the fellow in Mrs. Ryan's story made a bad confession; it seemed to me a great shame that people wouldn't stop criticizing him. I remember that steep hill down to the church, and the sunlit hillsides beyond the valley of the river, which I saw in the gaps between the houses like Adam's last glimpse of Paradise.

Then, when she had manœuvred me down the long flight of steps to the chapel yard, Nora suddenly changed her tone. She became the raging malicious devil she really was.

---

3. **covet** desire

"There you are!" she said with a yelp of triumph, hurling me through the church door. "And I hope he'll give you the penitential psalms,[4] you dirty little caffler."[5]

I knew then I was lost, given up to eternal justice. The door with the coloured-glass panels swung shut behind me, the sunlight went out and gave place to deep shadow, and the wind whistled outside so that the silence within seemed to crackle like ice under my feet. Nora sat in front of me by the confession box. There were a couple of old women ahead of her, and then a miserable-looking poor devil came and wedged me in at the other side, so that I couldn't escape even if I had the courage. He joined his hands and rolled his eyes in the direction of the roof, muttering aspirations in an anguished tone, and I wondered had he a grandmother too. Only a grand-mother could account for a fellow behaving in that heartbroken way, but he was better off than I, for he at least could go and confess his sins; while I would make a bad confession and then die in the night and be continually coming back and burning people's furniture.

Nora's turn came, and I heard the sound of something slamming, and then her voice as if butter wouldn't melt in her mouth, and then another slam, and out she came. God, the hypocrisy of women! Her eyes were low-ered, her head was bowed, and her hands were joined very low down on her stomach, and she walked up the aisle to the side altar looking like a saint. You never saw such an exhibition of devotion; and I remembered the devil-ish malice with which she had tormented me all the way from our door, and wondered were all religious people like that, really. It was my turn now. With the fear of damnation in my soul I went in, and the confessional door closed of itself behind me.

It was pitch-dark and I couldn't see priest or anything else. Then I really began to be frightened. In the darkness it was a matter between God and me, and He had all the odds. He knew what my intentions were before I even started; I had no chance. All I had ever been told about confession got mixed up in my mind, and I knelt to one wall and said: "Bless me, father, for I have sinned; this is my first confession." I waited for a few minutes, but nothing happened, so I tried it on the other wall. Nothing happened there either. He had me spotted all right.

It must have been then that I noticed the shelf at about one height with my head. It was really a place for grown-up people to rest their elbows, but in my distracted state I thought it was probably the place you were supposed to kneel. Of course, it was on the high side and not very deep, but I was al-ways good at climbing and managed to get up all right. Staying up was the

---

4. **penitential psalms** seven readings from the Old Testament of the Bible
5. **caffler** literally, a rag and bone dealer

trouble. There was room only for my knees, and nothing you could get a grip on but a sort of wooden moulding a bit above it. I held on to the moulding and repeated the words a little louder, and this time something happened all right. A slide was slammed back; a little light entered the box, and a man's voice said: "Who's there?"

"'Tis me, father," I said for fear he mightn't see me and go away again. I couldn't see him at all. The place the voice came from was under the moulding, about level with my knees, so I took a good grip of the moulding and swung myself down till I saw the astonished face of a young priest looking up at me. He had to put his head on one side to see me, and I had to put mine on one side to see him, so we were more or less talking to one another upside-down. It struck me as a queer way of hearing confessions, but I didn't feel it my place to criticize.

"Bless me, father, for I have sinned; this is my first confession," I rattled off all in one breath, and swung myself down the least shade more to make it easier for him.

"What are you doing up there?" he shouted in an angry voice, and the strain the politeness was putting on my hold of the moulding, and the shock of being addressed in such an uncivil tone, were too much for me. I lost my grip, tumbled, and hit the door an unmerciful wallop before I found myself flat on my back in the middle of the aisle. The people who had been waiting stood up with their mouths open. The priest opened the door of the middle box and came out, pushing his biretta[6] back from his forehead; he looked something terrible. Then Nora came scampering down the aisle.

"Oh, you dirty little caffler!" she said. "I might have known you'd do it. I might have known you'd disgrace me. I can't leave you out of my sight for one minute."

Before I could even get to my feet to defend myself she bent down and gave me a clip across the ear. This reminded me that I was so stunned I had even forgotten to cry, so that people might think I wasn't hurt at all, when in fact I was probably maimed for life. I gave a roar out of me.

"What's all this about?" the priest hissed, getting angrier than ever and pushing Nora off me. "How dare you hit the child like that, you little vixen?"

"But I can't do my penance[7] with him, father," Nora cried, cocking an outraged eye up at him.

"Well, go and do it, or I'll give you some more to do," he said, giving me a hand up. "Was it coming to confession you were, my poor man?" he asked me.

---

6. **biretta** stiff, square cap worn by Roman Catholic clergy
7. **penance** prayers said to atone for wrongdoing

"'Twas, father," said I with a sob.

"Oh," he said respectfully, "a big hefty fellow like you must have terrible sins. Is this your first?"

"'Tis, father," said I.

"Worse and worse," he said gloomily. "The crimes of a lifetime. I don't know will I get rid of you at all today. You'd better wait now till I'm finished with these old ones. You can see by the looks of them they haven't much to tell."

"I will, father," I said with something approaching joy.

The relief of it was really enormous. Nora stuck out her tongue at me from behind his back, but I couldn't even be bothered retorting.[8] I knew from the very moment that man opened his mouth that he was intelligent above the ordinary. When I had time to think, I saw how right I was. It only stood to reason that a fellow confessing after seven years would have more to tell than people that went every week. The crimes of a lifetime, exactly as he said. It was only what he expected, and the rest was the cackle of old women and girls with their talk of hell, the bishop, and the penitential psalms. That was all they knew. I started to make my examination of conscience, and barring the one bad business of my grandmother it didn't seem so bad.

The next time, the priest steered me into the confession box himself and left the shutter back the way I could see him get in and sit down at the further side of the grille from me.

"Well, now," he said, "what do they call you?"

"Jackie, father," said I.

"And what's a-trouble to you, Jackie?"

"Father," I said, feeling I might as well get it over while I had him in good humour, "I had it all arranged to kill my grandmother."

He seemed a bit shaken by that, all right, because he said nothing for quite a while.

"My goodness," he said at last, "that'd be a shocking thing to do. What put that into your head?"

"Father," I said, feeling very sorry for myself, "she's an awful woman."

"Is she?" he asked. "What way is she awful?"

"She takes porter, father," I said, knowing well from the way Mother talked of it that this was a mortal sin, and hoping it would make the priest take a more favourable view of my case.

"Oh, my!" he said, and I could see he was impressed.

"And snuff, father," said I.

"That's a bad case, sure enough, Jackie," he said.

---

8. retorting answering or responding

"And she goes round in her bare feet, father," I went on in a rush of self-pity, "and she know I don't like her, and she gives pennies to Nora and none to me, and my da sides with her and flakes me, and one night I was so heart-scalded I made up my mind I'd have to kill her."

"And what would you do with the body?" he asked with great interest.

"I was thinking I could chop that up and carry it away in a barrow I have," I said.

"Begor, Jackie," he said "do you know you're a terrible child?"

"I know, father," I said, for I was just thinking the same thing myself. "I tried to kill Nora too with a bread-knife under the table, only I missed her."

"Is that the little girl that was beating you just now?" he asked.

"'Tis, father."

"Someone will go for her with a bread-knife one day, and he won't miss her," he said rather cryptically. "You must have great courage. Between ourselves, there's a lot of people I'd like to do the same to but I'd never have the nerve. Hanging is an awful death."

"Is it, father?" I asked with the deepest interest—I was always very keen on hanging. "Did you ever see a fellow hanged?"

"Dozens of them," he said solemnly. "And they all died roaring."

"Jay!" I said.

"Oh, a horrible death!" he said with great satisfaction. "Lots of the fellows I saw killed their grandmothers too, but they all said 'twas never worth it."

He had me there for a full ten minutes talking, and then walked out the chapel yard with me. I was genuinely sorry to part with him, because he was the most entertaining character I'd ever met in the religious line. Outside, after the shadow of the church, the sunlight was like the roaring of waves on a beach; it dazzled me; and when the frozen silence melted and I heard the screech of trams on the road my heart soared. I knew now I wouldn't die in the night and come back, leaving marks on my mother's furniture. It would be a great worry to her, and the poor soul had enough.

Nora was sitting on the railing, waiting for me, and she put on a very sour puss when she saw the priest with me. She was mad jealous because a priest had never come out of the church with her.

"Well," she asked coldly, after he left me, "what did he give you?"

"Three Hail Marys," I said.

"Three Hail Marys," she repeated incredulously. "You mustn't have told him anything."

"I told him everything," I said confidently.

"About Gran and all?"

"About Gran and all."

(All she wanted was to be able to go home and say I'd made a bad confession.)

"Did you tell him you went for me with the bread-knife?" she asked with a frown.

"I did to be sure."

"And he only gave you three Hail Marys?"

"That's all."

She slowly got down from the railing with a baffled air. Clearly, this was beyond her. As we mounted the steps back to the main road she looked at me suspiciously.

"What are you sucking?" she asked.

"Bullseyes."

"Was it the priest gave them to you?"

"'Twas."

"Lord God," she wailed bitterly, "some people have all the luck! 'Tis no advantage to anybody trying to be good. I might just as well be a sinner like you."

**Richard
Rodriguez**

Aria: A Memoir of a Bilingual Childhood

*In this first-person essay, Rodriguez relates his experience
and his feelings about bilingual education.*

I REMEMBER, to start with, that day in Sacramento, in a California now
nearly thirty years past, when I first entered a classroom—able to understand
about fifty stray English words. The third of four children, I had been pre-
ceded by my older brother and sister to a neighborhood Roman Catholic
school. But neither of them had revealed very much about their classroom
experiences. They left each morning and returned each afternoon, always
together, speaking Spanish as they climbed the five steps to the porch. And
their mysterious books, wrapped in brown shopping-bag paper, remained on
the table next to the door, closed firmly behind them.

An accident of geography sent me to a school where all my classmates
were white and many were the children of doctors and lawyers and business
executives. On that first day of school, my classmates must certainly have
been uneasy to find themselves apart from their families, in the first institu-
tion of their lives. But I was astonished. I was fated to be the "problem student" in the class.

The nun said, in a friendly but oddly impersonal voice: "Boys and girls,
this is Richard Rodriguez." (I had heard her sound it out: *Rich-heard Road-
ree-guess.*) It was the first time I had heard anyone say my name in English.
"Richard," the nun repeated more slowly, writing my name down in her
book. Quickly I turned to see my mother's face dissolve in a watery blur behind the pebbled-glass door.

Now, many years later, I hear of something called "bilingual educa-tion"—a scheme proposed in the late 1960s by Hispanic-American social activists, later endorsed by a congressional vote. It is a program that seeks to permit non-English-speaking children (many from lower-class homes) to use their "family language" as the language of school. Such, at least, is the aim its supporters announce. I hear them, and am forced to say no: It is not possible for a child, any child, ever to use his family's language in school. Not to understand this is to misunderstand the public uses of schooling and to trivialize the nature of intimate life.

Memory teaches me what I know of these matters. The boy reminds the adult. I was a bilingual child, but of a certain kind: "socially disadvantaged," the son of working-class parents, both Mexican immigrants.

In the early years of my boyhood, my parents coped very well in America. My father had steady work. My mother managed at home. They were nobody's victims. When we moved to a house many blocks from the Mexican-American section of town, they were not intimidated by those two or three neighbors who initially tried to make us unwelcome. ("Keep your brats away from my sidewalk!") But despite all they achieved, or perhaps because they had so much to achieve, they lacked any deep feeling of ease, of belonging in public. They regarded the people at work or in crowds as being very distant from us. Those were the others, *los gringos*.[1] That term was interchangeable in their speech with another, even more telling: *los americanos*.

I grew up in a house where the only regular guests were my relations. On a certain day, enormous families of relatives would visit us, and there would be so many people that the noise and the bodies would spill out to the back-yard and onto the front porch. Then for weeks no one would come. (If the doorbell rang, it was usually a salesman.) Our house stood apart—gaudy yel-low in a row of white bungalows.[2] We were the people with the noisy dog, the people who raised chickens. We were the foreigners on the block. A few neighbors would smile and wave at us. We waved back. But until I was seven years old, I did not know the name of the old couple living next door or the names of the kids living across the street.

In public, my father and mother spoke a hesitant, accented, and not al-ways grammatical English. And then they would have to strain, their bodies tense, to catch the sense of what was rapidly said by *los gringos*. At home, they returned to Spanish. The language of their Mexican past sounded in counterpoint to the English spoken in public. The words would come quickly, with ease. Conveyed through those sounds was the pleasing,

---

1. *los gringos* non-Hispanic people
2. **bungalows** one-story houses with low-pitched roofs

soothing, consoling reminder that one was at home.

During those years when I was first learning to speak, my mother and father addressed me only in Spanish; in Spanish I learned to reply. By contrast, English (*inglés*) was the language I came to associate with gringos, rarely heard in the house. I learned my first words of English overhearing my parents speaking to strangers. At six years of age, I knew just enough words for my mother to trust me on errands to stores one block away—but no more.

I was then a listening child, careful to hear the very different sounds of Spanish and English. Wide-eyed with hearing, I'd listen to sounds more than to words. First, there were English (gringo) sounds. So many words still were unknown to me that when the butcher or the lady at the drugstore said something, exotic polysyllabic sounds would bloom in the midst of their sentences. Often the speech of people in public seemed to me very loud, booming with confidence. The man behind the counter would literally ask, "What can I do for you?" But by being so firm and clear, the sound of his voice said that he was a gringo, he belonged in public society. There were also the high, nasal notes of middle-class American speech—which I rarely am conscious of hearing today because I hear them so often, but could not stop hearing when I was a boy. Crowds at Safeway or at bus stops were noisy with the birdlike sounds of *los gringos*. I'd move away from them all—all the chirping chatter above me.

My own sounds I was unable to hear, but I knew that I spoke English poorly. My words could not extend to form complete thoughts. And the words I did speak I didn't know well enough to make distinct sounds. (Listeners would usually lower their heads to hear better what I was trying to say.) But it was one thing for me to speak English with difficulty; it was more troubling to hear my parents speaking in public: their high-whining vowels and guttural consonants; their sentences that got stuck with "eh" and "ah" sounds; the confused syntax; the hesitant rhythm of sounds so different from the way gringos spoke. I'd notice, moreover, that my parents' voices were softer than those of gringos we would meet.

I am tempted to say now that none of this mattered. (In adulthood I am embarrassed by childhood fears.) And, in a way, it didn't matter very much that my parents could not speak English with ease. Their linguistic difficulties had no serious consequences. My mother and father made themselves understood at the county hospital clinic and at government offices. And yet, in another way, it mattered very much. It was unsettling to hear my parents struggle with English. Hearing them, I'd grow nervous, and my clutching trust in their protection and power would be weakened.

There were many times like the night at a brightly lit gasoline station (a blaring white memory) when I stood uneasily hearing my father talk to a teenage attendant. I do not recall what they were saying, but I cannot forget the sounds my father made as he spoke. At one point his words slid together to form one long word—sounds as confused as the threads of blue and green oil in the puddle next to my shoes. His voice rushed through what he had left to say. Toward the end, he reached falsetto notes, appealing to his listener's understanding. I looked away at the lights of passing automobiles. I tried not to hear any more. But I heard only too well the attendant's reply, his calm, easy tones. Shortly afterward, headed for home, I shivered when my father put his hand on my shoulder. The very first chance I got, I evaded his grasp and ran on ahead into the dark, skipping with feigned boyish exuberance.[3]

But then there was Spanish: *español*, the language rarely heard away from the house; *español*, the language which seemed to me therefore a private language, my family's language. To hear its sounds was to feel myself specially recognized as one of the family, apart from *los otros*.[4] A simple remark, an inconsequential comment could convey that assurance. My parents would say something to me and I would feel embraced by the sounds of their words. Those sounds said: *I am speaking with ease in Spanish. I am addressing you in words I never use with los gringos. I recognize you as someone special, close, like no one outside. You belong with us. In the family. Ricardo.*

At the age of six, well past the time when most middle-class children no longer notice the difference between sounds uttered at home and words spoken in public, I had a different experience. I lived in a world compounded of sounds. I was a child longer than most. I lived in a magical world, surrounded by sounds both pleasing and fearful. I shared with my family a language enchantingly private—different from that used in the city around us.

Just opening or closing the screen door behind me was an important experience. I'd rarely leave home all alone or without feeling reluctance. Walking down the sidewalk, under the canopy of tall trees, I'd warily notice the (suddenly) silent neighborhood kids who stood warily watching me. Nervously, I'd arrive at the grocery store to hear there the sounds of the gringo, reminding me that in this so-big world I was a foreigner. But if leaving home was never routine, neither was coming back. Walking toward our house, climbing the steps from the sidewalk, in summer when the front door was open, I'd hear voices beyond the screen door talking in Spanish. For a second or two I'd stay, linger there listening. Smiling, I'd hear my mother call out, saying in Spanish, "Is that you, Richard?" Those were her words, but all the while her sounds would assure me: *You are home now. Come closer inside. With us.* "Sí," I'd reply.

---

3. **exuberance** enthusiasm or zest
4. **los otros** the others

Once more inside the house, I would resume my place in the family. The sounds would grow harder to hear. Once more at home, I would grow less conscious of them. It required, however, no more than the blurt of the door-bell to alert me all over again to listen to sounds. The house would turn instantly quiet while my mother went to the door. I'd hear her hard English sounds. I'd wait to hear her voice turn to soft-sounding Spanish, which assured me, as surely as did the clicking tongue of the lock on the door, that the stranger was gone.

Plainly it is not healthy to hear such sounds so often. It is not healthy to distinguish public from private sounds so easily. I remained cloistered by sounds, timid and shy in public, too dependent on the voices at home. And yet I was a very happy child when I was at home. I remember many nights when my father would come back from work, and I'd hear him call out to my mother in Spanish, sounding relieved. In Spanish, his voice would sound the light and free notes that he never could manage in English. Some nights I'd jump up just hearing his voice. My brother and I would come running into the room where he was with our mother. Our laughing (so deep was the pleasure!) became screaming. Like others who feel the pain of public alienation, we transformed the knowledge of our public separateness into a consoling reminder of our intimacy. Excited, our voices joined in a celebration of sounds. *We are speaking now the way we never speak out in public—we are together*, the sounds told me. Some nights no one seemed willing to loosen the hold that sounds had on us. At dinner we invented new words that sounded Spanish, but made sense only to us. We pieced together new words by taking, say, an English verb and giving it Spanish endings. My mother's instructions at bedtime would be lacquered with mock-urgent tones. Or a word like *sí*, sounded in several notes, would convey added measures of feeling. Tongues lingered around the edges of words, especially fat vowels. And we happily sounded that military drum roll, the twirling roar of the Spanish *r*. Family language, my family's sounds: the voices of my parents and sisters and brother. Their voices insisting: *You belong here. We are family members. Related. Special to one another. Listen!* Voices singing and sighing, rising and straining, then surging, teeming with pleasure which burst syllables into fragments of laughter. At times it seemed there was steady quiet only when, from another room, the rustling whispers of my parents faded and I edged closer to sleep.

Supporters of bilingual education imply today that students like me miss a great deal by not being taught in their family's language. What they seem not to recognize is that, as a socially disadvantaged child, I regarded Spanish as a private language. It was a ghetto language that deepened and strengthened my feeling of public separateness. What I needed to learn in school was that I had the right, and the obligation, to speak the public language. The odd truth is that my first-grade classmates could have become bilingual, in the conventional sense of the word, more easily than I. Had they been taught early (as upper middle-class children often are taught) a "second language" like Spanish or French, they could have regarded it simply as another public language. In my case, such bilingualism could not have been so quickly achieved. What I did not believe was that I could speak a single public language.

Without question, it would have pleased me to have heard my teachers address me in Spanish when I entered the classroom. I would have felt much less afraid. I would have imagined that my instructors were somehow "related" to me; I would indeed have heard their Spanish as my family's language. I would have trusted them and responded with ease. But I would have delayed—postponed for how long?—having to learn the language of public society. I would have evaded—and for how long?—learning the great lesson of school: that I had a public identity.

Fortunately, my teachers were unsentimental about their responsibility. What they understood was that I needed to speak public English. So their voices would search me out, asking me questions. Each time I heard them I'd look up in surprise to see a nun's face frowning at me. I'd mumble, not really meaning to answer. The nun would persist. "Richard, stand up. Don't look at the floor. Speak up. Speak to the entire class, not just to me!" But I couldn't believe English could be my language to use. (In part, I did not want to believe it.) I continued to mumble. I resisted the teacher's demands. (Did I somehow suspect that once I learned this public language my family life would be changed?) Silent, waiting for the bell to sound, I remained dazed, diffident, afraid.

Because I wrongly imagined that English was intrinsically[5] a public language and Spanish was intrinsically private, I easily noted the difference between classroom language and the language of home. At school, words were directed to a general audience of listeners. ("Boys and girls . . .") Words were meaningfully ordered. And the point was not self-expression alone, but to make oneself understood by many others. The teacher quizzed: "Boys and girls, why do we use that word in this sentence? Could we think of a better word to use there? Would the sentence change its meaning if the words were differently arranged? Isn't there a better way of saying much the same thing?" (I couldn't say. I wouldn't try to say.)

Three months passed. Five. A half a year. Unsmiling, ever watchful, my teachers noted my silence. They began to connect my behavior with the slow progress my brother and sisters were making. Until, one Saturday

---

5. **intrinsically** truly or really

morning, three nuns arrived at the house to talk to our parents. Stiffly they sat on the blue living-room sofa. From the doorway of another room, spying on the visitors, I noted the incongruity, the clash of two worlds, the faces and voices of school intruding upon the familiar setting of home. I overheard one voice gently wondering, "Do your children speak only Spanish at home, Mrs. Rodriguez?" While another voice added, "That Richard especially seems so timid and shy."

That Rich-heard!

With great tact, the visitors continued, "Is it possible for you and your husband to encourage your children to practice their English when they are home?" Of course my parents complied. What would they not do for their children's well-being? And how could they question the Church's authority which those women represented? In an instant they agreed to give up the language (the sounds) which had revealed and accentuated[6] our family's closeness. The moment after the visitors left, the change was observed. "*Ahora*, speak to us only *en inglés*,"[7] my father and mother told us.

At first, it seemed a kind of game. After dinner each night, the family gathered together to practice "our" English. It was still then *inglés*, a language foreign to us, so we felt drawn to it as strangers. Laughing, we would try to define words we could not pronounce. We played with strange English sounds, often over-anglicizing[8] our pronunciations. And we filled the smiling gaps of our sentences with familiar Spanish sounds. But that was cheating, somebody shouted, and everybody laughed.

In school, meanwhile, like my brother and sisters, I was required to attend a daily tutoring session. I needed a full year of this special work. I also needed my teachers to keep my attention from straying in class by calling out, "*Rich-heard!*"—their English voices slowly loosening the ties to my other name, with its three notes, *Ri-car-do*. Most of all, I needed to hear my mother and father speak to me in a moment of seriousness in "broken"—suddenly heartbreaking—English. This scene was inevitable. One Saturday morning I entered the kitchen where my parents were talking, but I did not realize that they were talking in Spanish until, the moment they saw me, their voices changed and they began speaking in English. The gringo sounds they uttered startled me. Pushed me away. In that moment of trivial misunderstanding and profound insight, I felt my throat twisted by unsounded grief. I simply turned and left the room. But I had no place to escape to where I could grieve in Spanish. My brother and sisters were speaking English in another part of the house.

---

6. **accentuated** stressed or emphasized
7. *Ahora,* **speak to us only** *en inglés* Now, speak to us only in English
8. **anglicizing** adapting a foreign word or phrase to English usage

Again and again in the days following, as I grew increasingly angry, I was obliged to hear my mother and father encouraging me: "Speak to us *en inglés*." Only then did I determine to learn classroom English. Thus, sometime afterward it happened: one day in school, I raised my hand to volunteer an answer to a question. I spoke out in a loud voice and I did not think it remarkable when the entire class understood. That day I moved very far from being the disadvantaged child I had been only days earlier. Taken hold at last was the belief, the calming assurance, that I *belonged* in public.

Shortly after, I stopped hearing the high, troubling sounds of *los gringos*. A more and more confident speaker of English, I didn't listen to how strangers sounded when they talked to me. With so many English-speaking people around me, I no longer heard American accents. Conversations quickened. Listening to persons whose voices sounded eccentrically pitched, I might note their sounds for a few seconds, but then I'd concentrate on what they were saying. Now when I heard someone's tone of voice— angry or questioning or sarcastic or happy or sad—I didn't distinguish it from the words it expressed. Sound and word were thus tightly wedded. At the end of each day I was often bemused, and always relieved, to realize how "soundless," though crowded with words, my day in public had been. An eight-year-old boy, I finally came to accept what had been technically true since my birth: I was an American citizen.

But diminished by then was the special feeling of closeness at home. Gone was the desperate, urgent, intense feeling of being at home among those with whom I felt intimate. Our family remained a loving family, but one greatly changed. We were no longer so close, no longer bound tightly together by the knowledge of our separateness from *los gringos*. Neither my older brother nor my sisters rushed home after school any more. Nor did I. When I arrived home, often there would be neighborhood kids in the house. Or the house would be empty of sounds.

Following the dramatic Americanization of their children, even my parents grew more publicly confident—especially my mother. First she learned the names of all the people on the block. Then she decided we needed to have a telephone in our house. My father, for his part, continued to use the word gringo, but it was no longer charged with bitterness or distrust. Stripped of any emotional content, the word simply became a name for those Americans not of Hispanic descent. Hearing him, sometimes, I wasn't sure if he was pronouncing the Spanish word *gringo*, or saying gringo in English.

There was a new silence at home. As we children learned more and more English, we shared fewer and fewer words with our parents. Sentences needed to be spoken slowly when one of us addressed our mother or father. Often the parent wouldn't understand. The child would need to repeat himself. Still the parent misunderstood. The young voice, frustrated, would end up saying, "Never mind"—the subject was closed. Dinners would be noisy with the clinking of knives and forks against dishes. My mother would smile softly between her remarks; my father, at the other end of the table, would chew and chew his food while he stared over the heads of his children.

My mother! My father! After English became my primary language, I no longer knew what words to use in addressing my parents. The old Spanish words (those tender accents of sound) I had earlier used—*mamá* and *papá*— I couldn't use any more. They would have been all-too-painful reminders of how much had changed in my life. On the other hand, the words I heard neighborhood kids call their parents seemed equally unsatisfactory. "Mother" and "father," "ma," "papa," "pa," "dad," "pop" (how I hated the all-American sound of that last word)—all these I felt were unsuitable terms of address for my *parents*. As a result, I never used them at home. Whenever I'd speak to my parents, I would try to get their attention by looking at them. In public conversations, I'd refer to them as my "parents" or my "mother" and "father."

My mother and father, for their part, responded differently, as their children spoke to them less. My mother grew restless, seemed troubled and anxious at the scarceness of words exchanged in the house. She would question me about my day when I came home from school. She smiled at my small talk. She pried at the edges of my sentences to get me to say something more. ("What . . .?") She'd join conversations she overheard, but her intrusions often stopped her children's talking. By contrast, my father seemed to grow reconciled to the new quiet. Though his English somewhat improved, he tended more and more to retire into silence. At dinner he spoke very little. One night his children and even his wife helplessly giggled at his garbled English pronunciation of the Catholic "Grace Before Meals." Thereafter he made his wife recite the prayer at the start of each meal, even on formal occasions when there were guests in the house.

Hers became the public voice of the family. On official business it was she, not my father, who would usually talk to strangers on the phone or in stores. We children grew so accustomed to his silence that years later we would routinely refer to his "shyness." (My mother often tried to explain: both of his parents died when he was eight. He was raised by an uncle who treated him as little more than a menial servant. He was never encouraged to speak. He grew up alone—a man of few words.) But I realized my father was not shy whenever I'd watch him speaking Spanish with relatives. Using Spanish, he was quickly effusive. Especially when talking with other men, his voice would spark, flicker, flare alive with varied sounds. In Spanish he expressed ideas and feelings he rarely revealed when speaking English. With firm Spanish sounds he conveyed a confidence and authority that English would never allow him.

The silence at home, however, was not simply the result of fewer words passing between parents and children. More profound for me was the silence created by my inattention to sounds. At about the time I no longer bothered to listen with care to the sounds of English in public, I grew careless about listening to the sounds made by the family when they spoke. Most of the time I would hear someone speaking at home and didn't distinguish his sounds from the words people uttered in public. I didn't even pay much attention to my parents' accented and ungrammatical speech—at least not at home. Only when I was with them in public would I become alert to their accents. But even then their sounds caused me less and less concern. For I was growing increasingly confident of my own public identity.

I would have been happier about my public success had I not recalled, sometimes, what it had been like earlier, when my family conveyed its intimacy through a set of conveniently private sounds. Sometimes in public, hearing a stranger, I'd hark back to my lost past. A Mexican farm worker approached me one day downtown. He wanted directions to some place. "*Hijito,* . . ."[9] he said. And his voice stirred old longings. Another time I was standing beside my mother in the visiting room of a Carmelite convent, before the dense screen which rendered the nuns shadowy figures. I heard several of them speaking Spanish in their busy, singsong, overlapping voices, assuring my mother that, yes, yes, we were remembered, all our family was remembered, in their prayers. Those voices echoed faraway family sounds. Another day a dark-faced old woman touched my shoulder lightly to steady herself as she boarded a bus. She murmured something to me I couldn't quite comprehend. Her Spanish voice came near, like the face of a never-before-seen relative in the instant before I was kissed. That voice, like so many of the Spanish voices I'd hear in public, recalled the golden age of my childhood.

Bilingual educators say today that children lose a degree of "individuality" by becoming assimilated into public society. (Bilingual schooling is a program popularized in the seventies, that decade when middle-class "ethnics" began to resist the process of assimilation—the "American melting pot.") But the bilingualists oversimplify when they scorn the value and necessity of assimilation. They do not seem to realize that a person is individualized in two ways. So they do not realize that, while one suffers a diminished sense of *private* individuality by being assimilated into public society, such assimilation makes possible the achievement of *public* individuality. Simplistically again, the bilingualists insist that a student should be

---

9. *Hijito* little boy, little son

reminded of his difference from others in mass society, of his "heritage." But they equate mere separateness with individuality. The fact is that only in private—with intimates—is separateness from the crowd a prerequisite for individuality; an intimate "tells" me that I am unique, unlike all others, apart from the crowd. In public, by contrast, full individuality is achieved, paradoxically, by those who are able to consider themselves members of the crowd. Thus it happened for me. Only when I was able to think of myself as an American, no longer an alien in gringo society, could I seek the rights and opportunities necessary for full public individuality. The social and po-litical advantages I enjoy as a man began on the day I came to believe that my name is indeed *Rich-heard Road-ree-guess.* It is true that my public society today is often impersonal; in fact, my public society is usually mass society. But despite the anonymity of the crowd, and despite the fact that the indi-viduality I achieve in public is often tenuous—because it depends on my being one in a crowd—I celebrate the day I acquired my new name. Those middle-class ethnics who scorn assimilation seem to me filled with decadent self-pity, obsessed by the burden of public life. Dangerously, they romanti-cize public separateness and trivialize the dilemma of those who are truly socially disadvantaged.

If I rehearse here the changes in my private life after my Americanization, it is finally to emphasize a public gain. The loss implies the gain. The house I returned to each afternoon was quiet. Intimate sounds no longer greeted me at the door. Inside there were other noises. The tele-phone rang. Neighborhood kids ran past the door of the bedroom where I was reading my schoolbooks—covered with brown shopping-bag paper. Once I learned the public language, it would never again be easy for me to hear intimate family voices. More and more of my day was spent hearing words, not sounds. But that may only be a way of saying that on the day I raised my hand in class and spoke loudly to an entire roomful of faces, my childhood started to end.

I grew up the victim of a disconcerting confusion. As I became fluent in English, I could no longer speak Spanish with confidence. I continued to understand spoken Spanish, and in high school I learned how to read and write Spanish. But for many years I could not pronounce it. A powerful guilt blocked my spoken words; an essential glue was missing whenever I would try to connect words to form sentences. I would be unable to break a barrier of sound, to speak freely. I would speak, or try to speak, Spanish, and I would manage to utter halting, hiccuping sounds which betrayed my unease. (Even today I speak Spanish very slowly, at best.)

When relatives and Spanish-speaking friends of my parents came to the house, my brother and sisters would usually manage to say a few words before being excused. I never managed so gracefully. Each time I'd hear myself addressed in Spanish, I couldn't respond with any success. I'd know the words I wanted to say, but I couldn't say them. I would try to speak, but everything I said seemed to me horribly anglicized. My mouth wouldn't form the sounds right. My jaw would tremble. After a phrase or two, I'd stutter, cough up a warm, silvery sound, and stop.

My listeners were surprised to hear me. They'd lower their heads to grasp better what I was trying to say. They would repeat their questions in gentle, affectionate voices. But then I would answer in English. No, no, they would say, we want you to speak to us in Spanish ("*en español*"). But I couldn't do it. Then they would call me *pocho*. Sometimes playfully, teasing, using the tender diminutive—*mi pochito*. Sometimes not so playfully but mockingly, *pocho*. (A Spanish dictionary defines that word as an adjective meaning "colorless" or "bland." But I heard it as a noun, naming the Mexican-American who, in becoming an American, forgets his native society.) "*¡Pocho!*" my mother's best friend muttered, shaking her head. And my mother laughed, somewhere behind me. She said that her children didn't want to practice "our Spanish" after they started going to school. My mother's smiling voice made me suspect that the lady who faced me was not really angry at me. But searching her face, I couldn't find the hint of a smile.

Embarrassed, my parents would often need to explain their children's inability to speak fluent Spanish during those years. My mother encountered the wrath of her brother, her only brother, when he came up from Mexico one summer with his family and saw his nieces and nephews for the very first time. After listening to me, he looked away and said what a disgrace it was that my siblings and I couldn't speak Spanish, "*su propria idioma*."[10] He made that remark to my mother, but I noticed that he stared at my father.

One other visitor from those years I clearly remember: a long-time friend of my father from San Francisco who came to stay with us for several days in late August. He took great interest in me after he realized that I couldn't answer his questions in Spanish. He would grab me, as I started to leave the kitchen. He would ask me something. Usually he wouldn't bother to wait for my mumbled response. Knowingly, he'd murmur, "*¿Ay, pocho, pocho, dónde vas?*"[11] And he would press his thumbs into the upper part of my arms, making me squirm with pain. Dumbly I'd stand there, waiting for his wife to notice us and call him off with a benign smile. I'd giggle, hoping to deflate the tension between us, pretending that I hadn't seen the glittering scorn in his glance.

I recount such incidents only because they suggest the fierce power that

---

10. *su propria idioma*   their own language
11. *¿Ay, pocho, pocho, dónde vas?*   Pocho, where are you?

Spanish had over many people I met at home, how strongly Spanish was associated with closeness. Most of those people who called me a *pocho* could have spoken English to me, but many wouldn't. They seemed to think that Spanish was the only language we could use among ourselves, that Spanish alone permitted our association. (Such persons are always vulnerable to the ghetto merchant and the politician who have learned the value of speaking their clients' "family language" so as to gain immediate trust.) For my part, I felt that by learning English I had somehow committed a sin of betrayal. But betrayal against whom? Not exactly against the visitors to the house. Rather, I felt I had betrayed my immediate family. I knew that my parents had encouraged me to learn English. I knew that I had turned to English with angry reluctance. But once I spoke English with ease, I came to feel guilty. I sensed that I had broken the spell of intimacy which had once held the family so close together. It was this original sin against my family that I recalled whenever anyone addressed me in Spanish and I responded, confounded.

Yet even during those years of guilt, I was coming to grasp certain consoling truths about language and intimacy—truths that I learned gradually. Once, I remember playing with a friend in the backyard when my grandmother appeared at the window. Her face was stern with suspicion when she saw the boy (the *gringo* boy) I was with. She called out to me in Spanish, sounding the whistle of her ancient breath. My companion looked up and watched her intently as she lowered the window and moved (still visible) behind the light curtain, watching us both. He wanted to know what she had said. I started to tell him, to translate her Spanish words into English. The problem was, however, that though I knew how to translate exactly what she had told me, I realized that any translation would distort the deepest meaning of her message; it had been directed only to me. This message of intimacy could never be translated because it did not lie in the actual words she had used but passed through them. So any translation would have seemed wrong; the words would have been stripped of an essential meaning. Finally I decided not to tell my friend anything—just that I didn't hear all she had said.

This insight was unfolded in time. As I made more and more friends outside my house, I began to recognize intimate messages spoken in English in a close friend's confidential tone or secretive whisper. Even more remarkable were those instances when, apparently for no special reason, I'd become conscious of the fact that my companion was speaking *only to me*. I'd marvel then, just hearing his voice. It was a stunning event to be able to break through the barrier of public silence, to be able to hear the voice of the other, to realize that it was directed just to me. After such moments of intimacy outside the house, I began to trust what I heard intimately conveyed through my family's English. Voices at home at last punctured sad confusion. I'd hear myself addressed as an intimate—in English. Such moments were never as raucous[12] with sound as in past times, when we had used our "private" Spanish. (Our English-sounding house was never to be as noisy as our Spanish-sounding house had been.) Intimate moments were usually moments of soft sound. My mother would be ironing in the dining room while I did my homework nearby. She would look over at me, smile, and her voice sounded to tell me that I was her son. *Richard.*

Intimacy thus continued at home; intimacy was not stilled by English. Though there were fewer occasions for it—a change in my life that I would never forget—there were also times when I sensed the deep truth about language and intimacy: *Intimacy is not created by a particular language; it is created by intimates.* Thus the great change in my life was not linguistic but social. If, after becoming a successful student, I no longer heard intimate voices as often as I had earlier, it was not because I spoke English instead of Spanish. It was because I spoke public language for most of my day. I moved easily at last, a citizen in a crowded city of words. . . .

The child reminds the adult: to seek intimate sounds is to seek the company of intimates. I do not expect to hear those sounds in public. I would dishonor those I have loved, and those I love now, to claim anything else. I would dishonor our intimacy by holding on to a particular language and calling it my family language. Intimacy cannot be trapped within words; it passes through words. It passes. Intimates leave the room. Doors close. Faces move away from the window. Time passes, and voices recede into the dark. Death finally quiets the voice. There is no way to deny it, no way to stand in the crowd claiming to utter one's family language.

The last time I saw my grandmother I was nine years old. I can tell you some of the things she said to me as I stood by her bed, but I cannot quote the message of intimacy she conveyed with her voice. She laughed, holding my hand. Her voice illumined disjointed memories as it passed them again. She remembered her husband—his green eyes, his magic name of Narcissio, his early death. She remembered the farm in Mexico, the eucalyptus trees nearby (their scent, she remembered, like incense). She remembered the family cow, the bell around its neck heard miles away. A dog. She remembered working as a seamstress, how she'd leave her daughters and son for long hours to go into Guadalajara to work. And how my mother would come running toward her in the sun—in her bright yellow dress—on her return. "MMMMAAAAMMMMÁÁÁÁÁ," the old lady mimicked her daughter (my mother) to her daughter's son. She laughed. There was the

---

12. **raucous** noisy or loud

snap of a cough. An aunt came into the room and told me it was time I should leave. "You can see her tomorrow," she promised. So I kissed my grandmother's cracked face. And the last thing I saw was her thin, oddly youthful thigh, as my aunt rearranged the sheet on the bed.

At the funeral parlor a few days after, I remember kneeling with my relatives during the rosary. Among their voices I traced, then lost, the sounds of individual aunts in the surge of the common prayer. And I heard at that moment what since I have heard very often—the sound the women in my family make when they are praying in sadness. When I went up to look at my grandmother, I saw her through the haze of a veil draped over the open lid of the casket. Her face looked calm—but distant and unyielding to love. It was not the face I remembered seeing most often. It was the face she made in public when the clerk at Safeway asked her some question and I would need to respond. It was her public face that the mortician had designed with his dubious art.